# Guidelines

## for Microsoft® Office 365

### 2019 Edition

# Review and Assessment

## Anita Verno | Jan Marrelli

Bergen Community College
Paramus, New Jersey

Author and Consultant
Sault Ste. Marie, Ontario

PARADIGM
EDUCATION SOLUTIONS

St. Paul

**Vice President, Content and Digital Solutions:** Christine Hurney
**Director of Content Development, Computer Technology:** Cheryl Drivdahl
**Developmental Editor:** Katrina Lee
**Testers:** J. Neal Anthony and Melinda (Mindy) Shirey
**Director of Production:** Timothy W. Larson
**Production Editor:** Carrie Rogers
**Senior Design and Production Specialist:** Valerie A. King
**Copy Editor:** Christine Crabb
**Proofreader:** Shannon Kottke
**Vice President, Director of Digital Products:** Chuck Bratton
**Digital Projects Manager:** Tom Modl
**Digital Solutions Manager:** Gerry Yumul
**Senior Director of Digital Products and Onboarding:** Christopher Johnson
**Supervisor of Digital Products and Onboarding:** Ryan Isdahl
**Vice President, Marketing:** Lara Weber McLellan
**Marketing and Communications Manager:** Selena Hicks

Care has been taken to verify the accuracy of information presented in this book. However, the authors, editors, and publisher cannot accept responsibility for web, email, newsgroup, or chat room subject matter or content, or for consequences from the application of the information in this book, and make no warranty, expressed or implied, with respect to its content.

Trademarks: Microsoft is a trademark or registered trademark of Microsoft Corporation in the United States and/or other countries. Some of the product names and company names included in this book have been used for identification purposes only and may be trademarks or registered trade names of their respective manufacturers and sellers. The authors, editors, and publisher disclaim any affiliation, association, or connection with, or sponsorship or endorsement by, such owners.

Paradigm Education Solutions is independent from Microsoft Corporation and not affiliated with Microsoft in any manner.

**Cover Illustration Credit:** © nico_blue/gettyimages

We have made every effort to trace the ownership of all copyrighted material and to secure permission from copyright holders. In the event of any question arising as to the use of any material, we will be pleased to make the necessary corrections in future printings.

ISBN 978-0-76388-682-0 (print)
ISBN 978-0-76388-680-6 (digital)

Printed in the United States of America

28 27 26 25 24 23 22 21 20 19   1 2 3 4 5 6 7 8 9 10

# Contents

**Unit 1** **Getting Started**................................................1

    **Chapter 1** Computing Essentials...............................1

    **Chapter 2** Working with Student Data Files...............1

**Unit 2** **Office Application Basics**...............................3

**Unit 3** **Outlook**...................................................5

**Unit 4** **Word**........................................................7

    **Chapter 1** Creating Documents ...............................8

    **Chapter 2** Formatting Documents and Citing Sources .............12

    **Chapter 3** Working with Tables and Objects ...............18

    **Chapter 4** Finalizing and Sharing Documents ...............25

**Unit 5** **Excel**........................................................**35**

    **Chapter 1** Creating an Excel Workbook ...............36

    **Chapter 2** Working with Formulas and Functions ...............40

    **Chapter 3** Formatting Cells ...............45

    **Chapter 4** Working with Charts ...............49

**Unit 6** **Access**......................................................**59**

    **Chapter 1** Working with Databases ...............60

    **Chapter 2** Creating Forms and Tables ...............64

    **Chapter 3** Working with Queries and Reports ...............69

**Unit 7** **PowerPoint**............................................**83**

    **Chapter 1** Creating a Presentation ...............84

    **Chapter 2** Adding Media Elements and Effects ...............89

    **Chapter 3** Customizing a Slide Show ...............95

    **Chapter 4** Completing, Running, and Sharing Your Show ...............100

**Unit 8** **Integrating Office Applications**...............**111**

# UNIT 1

## Getting Started
## Review and Assessment

Chapter 1    **Understanding Computing Essentials**

Chapter 2    **Working with Student Data Files**

 The online course includes additional review and assessment resources.

 **Study Quiz**
*Online courseware includes Study Quizzes for Chapters 1 and 2.*

# UNIT 2

# Office Application Basics
# Review and Assessment

 **Study Quiz**
*Online courseware includes a Study Quiz.*

 The online course includes additional review and assessment resources.

# UNIT 3

## Outlook
## Review and Assessment

 **Study Quiz**
*Online courseware includes a Study Quiz.*

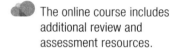 The online course includes additional review and assessment resources.

# UNIT 4

# Word Review and Assessment

Chapter 1    Creating Documents

Chapter 2    Formatting Documents and Citing Sources

Chapter 3    Working with Tables and Objects

Chapter 4    Finalizing and Sharing Documents

Unit 4 Skills Assessment

 The online course includes additional review and assessment resources.

# Word Review and Assessment

## Chapter 1 Creating Documents

### Study Quiz

*Online courseware includes a Study Quiz.*

### Features Review

*Online courseware includes a Features Review consisting of 10 multiple-choice questions to help reinforce your understanding of the chapter content.*

### Skills Review 1   Checking Spelling and Grammar and Proofreading a Blog Post

**Skills**   **CH1:** Enter and edit text; use cut, copy, and paste; perform a spelling and grammar check; and set margins

**Scenario**   You host the blog *Healthy Techie* and have just drafted a post that discusses the importance of thumbs for today's smartphone users. Use Editor to correct the paragraph, and then proofread for errors that are not caught by Editor.

**Steps**

1   Open the student data file named **C1R1-Thumbs** and save the file as **C1R1-Thumbs-Lastname**, but replace *Lastname* with your last name.

2   Type your name, a comma, and the current date (*MM-DD-YYYY format*) on the first line of the document, and then press Enter.

3   Use the spelling and grammar checker to correct errors in the text.

4   Move the last sentence, which begins *Thumbs play an*, to the start of the paragraph.

5   Change the margins to the *Wide* option.

6   Proofread the document and make any corrections.

7   Save the file.

8   Print or submit the completed file as directed by your instructor.

*Completed Review 1*

Student Name, Current Date

Thumbs play an important role in today's technological world as they allow you to type quickly on your smartphone. Current research shows the increased use of our thumbs has actually resulted in a change in the way thumbs and brains communicate. This not only shows how adaptable the brain is but highlights the tremendous amount of time individuals are spending on repetitive movement. Frequent repetitive movement, however, can result in medical issues. For example, carpal tunnel syndrome is associated with overuse of smartphones. To avoid carpal tunnel syndrome, limit your texting, take breaks from texting, and be sure to stretch your fingers, wrists, and forearms.

## Skills Review 2  Downloading and Modifying a Template for a Customer Service Complaint Letter

**Skills**    **CH1:** Enter and edit text, perform a spelling and grammar check, and create a document based on a template

**Scenario**  You just received your annual bill for auto insurance and are surprised by the dramatic increase in premiums. You decide to send a letter of complaint to the president of your insurance company. You want to format your letter properly and to include all the necessary information to ensure that it receives the attention it deserves.

**Steps**

1  Download the Letter complaining about customer service template. You will need to search for the template using the phrase *customer service complaint*. **Hint:** *In the New backstage area, type* customer service complaint *in the search box and then press Enter.*

2  In the *Your Name* placeholder, type your name. **Note:** *The second* Your Name *placeholder automatically updates with this information.*

3  Type the street address, city, state, zip code, phone, and email for your school in the appropriate placeholders.

4  In the *Date* placeholder, type the current date (*August 29, 2021* format).

5  In the *Recipient Name* placeholder, type Ava Macintosh. **Note:** *The second* Recipient Name *placeholder automatically updates with this information.*

6  Ava Macintosh is the president of ABC Insurance Company. Enter her title and the company name in the appropriate placeholders.

7  In the *Street Address* placeholder, type 123 Maple Street.

8  In the *City, ST, ZIP Code* placeholder, type St. Paul, MN 55102.

9  In the *Representative Name* placeholder, type Spencer West.

10  In the *Date* placeholder, type yesterday's date.

11  In the *Product or Service* placeholder, type my insurance policy.

12  Click *I am* in last sentence of the first paragraph, press the space bar, and then type, was no help to me.

13  In the *returning or canceling* placeholder, type canceling.

14  Use the spelling and grammar checker to locate and correct errors. Proofread the document to be sure it is correct.

15  Save the file with the name **C1R2-Insurance-Lastname**, but replace *Lastname* with your last name.

16  Print or submit the completed file as directed by your instructor.

 Skills Review 3 **Changing Document Properties and Inserting Elements into a Breakfast Plan**

**Skills** **CH1:** Enter and edit text; use the Show/Hide ¶ feature; use cut, copy, and paste; perform a spelling and grammar check; indent and add tabs using the ruler; insert a page break; and insert headers and footers

**Scenario** In an effort to get to class on time, you often run out the door without eating breakfast. Last week, you and a friend challenged each other to train for a half marathon, and you now realize that you need a quick, healthy breakfast for energy to survive your busy morning at school—and your afternoon training session!

**Steps**

1 Open the student data file named **C1R3-Breakfast** and save it as **C1R3-Breakfast-Lastname**, but replace *Lastname* with your last name.

2 Turn on Show/Hide ¶ to display formatting marks. ***Note:*** *Working with Show/Hide ¶ on is helpful throughout this review exercise.*

3 Insert a header that includes your name at the left margin and the current date (*MM-DD-YYYY format*) at the right margin. ***Hint:*** *Click the Insert tab, click the Header button in the Header & Footer group, and then click the* Blank (Three Columns) *option. Use the left and right placeholders, and delete the center placeholder.*

4   Add a footer that places a plain page number in the bottom center of the page.

5   On the first breakfast option line, which begins *2 fried eggs*, type Approximate calories before the number *500*. Be sure to include a space between the *s* at the end of *calories* and the *5* at the beginning of *500*.

6   Select the text you just typed—*Approximate calories*—copy it, and paste it before the number at the end of each of the next five breakfast options, from *Scrambled eggs with* through *Fruit salad*. Again, be sure you include a space between the *s* at the end of *calories* and the first digit of the number.

7   Select the list of breakfast options and its corresponding data, beginning with *2 fried eggs* and ending with *Approximate calories 210*. Set left tabs at 2.25 inches and 4.75 inches. **Hint:** *You may need to make the ruler visible.*

8   Indent the first line of the paragraph that begins with *Breakfast is an* by 0.5 inches. **Hint:** *See the Taking It Further sidebar in Skill 6.*

9   Insert a page break at the start of the line that begins *A few breakfast.*

10  Use the spelling and grammar checker to correct any spelling and grammar errors in the text.

11  Turn off Show/Hide ¶ and then proofread the document to be sure it is correct.

12  Save the file.

13  Print or submit the completed file as directed by your instructor.

### *Completed Review 3*

## Chapter 2
## Formatting Documents and Citing Sources

### Study Quiz
*Online courseware includes a Study Quiz.*

### Features Review
*Online courseware includes a Features Review consisting of 10 multiple-choice questions to help reinforce your understanding of the chapter content.*

### Skills Review 1 **Formatting an Essay about Exercise Equipment**

**Skills**  **CH1:** Enter and edit text, and insert headers and footers **CH2:** Change font and font size, use formatting tools, apply styles, align text, format paragraph and line spacing, format text in columns, copy formatting with Format Painter, and insert a footnote

**Scenario**  You have written a brief essay about exercise equipment for your community's Healthy Living initiative. Use various formatting tools to highlight important information in the document.

**Steps**

1 Open the student data file named **C2R1-Equipment** and save the file as **C2R1-Equipment-Lastname**, but replace *Lastname* with your last name.

2 Insert a header that includes your name at the left margin and the current date at the right margin.

3 Insert a footer with a plain page number in the center.

4 Select the title *Exercise Equipment* and change the style to Heading 1. Increase the font size to 22 points.

5 Justify the entire document. **Hint:** *Select all the text in the document and then change the alignment.*

6 Format the list of various types of exercise equipment (from *Treadmill* to *Balance board*) in three columns of equal width. **Hint:** *Turn on Show/Hide ¶ to be sure you select all the equipment names and their paragraph marks.*

7 Set the line spacing for the body of the document—beginning with *Exercise equipment includes* and ending with *exercise program!*—to 1.15. **Hint:** *Select the specified text and then change the line spacing.*

8 Select the two paragraphs at the start of the document body—beginning with *Exercise equipment includes* and ending with *as the following:*—and set the spacing after paragraphs to 12 points.

9 In the body of the document—beginning with *Exercise equipment includes* and ending with *as the following:*—italicize all four instances of the word equipment. **Hint:** *Italicize the first instance. Double-click the Format Painter button and then double-click the second instance; the second instance automatically adopts the same formatting as the first. Continue in this manner until you have italicized all instances of equipment. Click the Format Painter button again to turn off the feature.*

10 Insert a blank line above the final sentence of the document, which begins *Remember to check*.

11 Select the final sentence of the document, and then change the font size to 14 points and apply bold formatting.

12 Insert a footnote after the word *resistance* in the second sentence of the first paragraph (the sentence that begins *Exercise equipment may*). Type the body of the footnote as Resistance equipment uses weights and pulleys to permit individual adjustment.

13 Insert a footnote after the period that ends the second sentence of the first paragraph (the sentence that begins *Exercise equipment may*). Type the body of the footnote as Modern exercise equipment typically provides the ability to select the type of workout desired.

14 Save the file.

15 Print or submit the completed file as directed by your instructor.

### *Completed Review 1*

Student Name                                                                  Current Date

## Exercise Equipment

Exercise *equipment* includes any device used during physical activity that helps you gain strength, balance, and overall conditioning. Exercise *equipment* may enhance physical activity by allowing you to adjust resistance[1] and select from a menu of workout programs.[2] Although you can exercise without a device, you may find it easier to target a particular muscle group using *equipment*.

Whether you belong to a gym or have a home gym, you may want to use exercise *equipment* such as the following:

| | | |
|---|---|---|
| Treadmill | Yoga mat | Pull-up bar |
| Elliptical machine | Weight bench | Jump rope |
| Exercise bike | Weight set | Tension band |
| Rowing machine | Medicine ball | Balance board |
| Trampoline | Kettlebell | |

**Remember to check with a physician before beginning any new exercise program!**

---
[1] Resistance equipment uses weights and pulleys to permit individual adjustment.
[2] Modern exercise equipment typically provides the ability to select the type of workout desired.

1

**Skills Review 2** **Formatting a List of Exercises and Estimated Average Calories Burned**

**Skills**      **CH1:** Enter and edit text, use the Show/Hide ¶ feature, and insert headers and footers **CH2:** Change font and font size, use formatting tools, align text, create bulleted and numbered lists, and copy formatting with Format Painter

**Scenario**   You have drafted a paragraph listing a variety of exercise options and the estimated number of calories each burns for the average individual. Your community's Healthy Living initiative would like to post this list to help people understand how calories burned are related to different types of exercise. To make it easier for readers to see this connection, you decide to separate the activities and format them in a bulleted list.

**Steps**

1   Open the student data file named **C2R2-Calories** and save the file as **C2R2-Calories-Lastname**, but replace *Lastname* with your last name.

2   Insert a header that includes your name at the left margin and the current date at the right margin.

3   Insert a footer with a plain page number in the center.

4   Turn on Show/Hide ¶ to display formatting marks, and then separate the statements in the main body of the document (the paragraph beginning *After 30 minutes* and ending *burns 150 calories.*) into individual list items. ***Hint:*** *Delete the space before each statement, and then press Enter to place each statement on its own line.*

5   Add bullets to the list of statements beginning with *After 30 minutes* and ending with *Dancing for 30 minutes burns 150 calories.* Change the bullets to check marks. Change the font of the bulleted items to 16-point Calibri.

6   Change the font of the title *Burning Calories* to 28-point Lucida Sans, center the title, and change the font color to Green. ***Hint:*** *Click the Font Color button arrow and select the* Green *option in the* Standard Colors *section.*

7   Use Format Painter to apply the title formatting to the final sentence of the document, which begins *Find something you.* Italicize the last sentence.

8   Save the file.

9   Print or submit the completed file as directed by your instructor.

**Completed Review 2**

> Student Name                                    Current Date
>
> ### Burning Calories
>
> ✓ After 30 minutes of cross-country skiing, you burn up that plate of spaghetti with meat sauce and Parmesan cheese—about 450 calories.
> ✓ Thirty minutes on an indoor skiing machine offers the same benefits as 30 minutes of cross-country skiing—about 450 calories.
> ✓ Walking at around 4 miles per hour for 30 minutes burns 180 calories.
> ✓ Playing active, competitive tennis for 30 minutes burns 270 calories.
> ✓ Vacuuming the house for 30 minutes burns 90 calories.
> ✓ Running for 30 minutes burns 300 calories.
> ✓ Playing a twosome of golf for 30 minutes burns 80 calories.
> ✓ Weeding the garden for 30 minutes burns 150 calories.
> ✓ Inline skating or roller skating at a moderate pace for 30 minutes burns 210 calories.
> ✓ Dancing for 30 minutes burns 150 calories.
>
> *Find something you enjoy doing and burn some calories!*
>
> 1

## Skills Review 3 **Formatting a Report on How Yoga Benefits Families**

**Skills**    **CH1:** Enter and edit text, use the Show/Hide ¶ feature; insert a page break, and insert headers and footers **CH2:** Change font and font size, use formatting tools, align text, format paragraph and line spacing, insert citations using professional styles, and create a Works Cited page

**Scenario**    Your instructor has provided you with a draft of another student's term paper about the benefits of yoga and has given you the assignment of formatting the report for final submission. Your instructor has provided the following formatting guidelines:

*Font:* 12-point Times New Roman
*Spacing:* double
*Alignment:* left
*Paragraph first line indentation:* 0.5 inch
*Header:* your last name, a space, and the page number in the upper right corner
*References:* MLA Seventh Edition parenthetical citations
*Works Cited page:* required

**Steps**

1  Open the student data file **C2R3-Yoga** and save the file as **C2R3-Yoga-Lastname**, but replace *Lastname* with your last name.

2  Change the font for the entire document to 12-point Times New Roman.

3  Remove all blank lines. Set line spacing to double for the document. ***Hint:*** *Click the Show/Hide ¶ button to turn on the display of formatting marks, delete each extra paragraph mark, and then click the Show/Hide ¶ button again if you wish to work with it off.*

4  Highlight the body of the document—from the paragraph beginning *One way families* through the paragraph ending *from these advantages.*—and set paragraph indents and alignment as directed in the formatting guidelines given in the scenario above.

5  At the top of page 1, complete the following tasks:
    a. Replace *Instructor's Name* with the name of your instructor.
    b. Replace *Course Name* with the name of your course.
    c. Replace *Current Date* with today's date written in the *day month year* format (e.g., *5 March 2021*).

6  Type your name in parentheses after the author's name, *Julia Sanders,* replacing the words Student Name. ***Note:*** *Julia Sanders is the author of this paper. By enclosing your name in parentheses in this exercise, you are indicating that you modified the paper. When you write your own paper using* MLA Seventh Edition *style, you will type your own name as author and will not enclose it in parentheses.*

7  Center the title, *Improving Activity Levels in All Families through Yoga.*

8  Insert a blank header that contains your last name followed by a space and the page number. ***Hint:*** *Insert a Blank header (contains one field or placeholder), type your last name, type a space, and then use the Page Number button to insert a plain page number at the current position.* Make sure there is a blank line as the second line of the header. Right-align the header. The header font should be the same as in the rest of the document: 12-point Times New Roman.

9  Set the reference style to *MLA Seventh Edition.*

10  Add the following sources:

| *Type of Source* | *Book Section* |
|---|---|
| *Author* | Tanasi, A.; Videira, C.; Newcomb, J.; Diaz, A. |
| *Book Title* | Behavior management: Traditional and expanded approaches |

| | |
|---|---|
| Year | 2013 |
| Pages | 124-139 |
| City | Landham, MD |
| Publisher | University Press of America, Inc. |
| | |
| Type of Source | **Book** |
| Author | Gillen, L.; Gillen, J. |
| Title | Yoga Calm for Children: Educating Heart, Mind, and Body |
| Year | 2008 |
| City | Portland, OR |
| Publisher | Three Pebbles Press, LLC |

11 The following sources have values for both default fields and optional bibliography fields. For each source, enter data in the default fields that appear. Next, insert a check mark in the *Show All Bibliography Fields* check box and enter the values for the optional fields.

| | |
|---|---|
| Type of Source | *Journal Article* |
| Author | Satvika, G.; Buckley-Reed, A.; Alexander, L.; Chintakrindi, R.; Venice, L.; Patten Koenig, K. |
| Title | The effectiveness of a manualized yoga intervention on classroom behaviors in elementary school children with disabilities: A pilot study |
| Journal Name | Journal of Occupational Therapy, Schools, & Early Intervention |
| Year | 2013 |
| Pages | 158-164 |
| Volume (use optional field) | 6 |
| DOI (use optional field) | 10.1080/19411243.2013.810942 |
| | |
| Type of Source | *Journal Article* |
| Author | Hagins, M.; Haden, S.; Daly, L. |
| Title | A randomized controlled trial on the effects of yoga on stress reactivity in 6th grade students |
| Journal Name | Evidence-Based Complementary and Alternative Medicine |
| Year | 2013 |
| Volume (use optional field) | 2013 |
| DOI (use optional field) | 10.1155/2013/607134 |
| | |
| Type of Source | *Web site* |
| Author | Tilak, V. |
| Name of Web Page | The Benefits of Yoga for Kids |
| Year Accessed | 2013 |
| URL (use optional field) | http://www.parents.com/fun/sports/exercise/the-benefits-of-yoga-for-kids/ |

12 Enter the citations in the indicated locations using the Insert Citation button. ***Hint:*** *When replacing the citation placeholder text, do not delete the period.*

13 Place the insertion point at the end of the document and then insert a page break.

14 Use the Bibliography tool to create a Works Cited page. ***Hint:*** *Click* Works Cited *in the* Bibliography *drop-down list on the References tab.*

15 If necessary, modify the format of the Works Cited page so it conforms to the requirements of *MLA Seventh Edition*. Center the heading *Works Cited* and double-space the entire Works Cited section, beginning with the title and ending with the last line of the last citation. Format the Works Cited page in 12-point Times New Roman.

16 Save the file.

17 Print or submit the completed file as directed by your instructor.

Lastname 1

Julia Sanders (Student Name)

Instructor's Name

Course Name

Current Date

Improving Activity Levels in All Families through Yoga

One way families can improve activity level is through yoga. Yoga is a mind-body approach that has been shown to have positive influences on children and adults (Satvika, Buckley-Reed and Alexander). According to Tanasi, et al., yoga consists of physical movement, mental awareness, and spiritual connection. Hagins, Haden, and Daly define yoga as "an ancient tradition that uses techniques of posture (asana), breath control (pranayauna), and meditation, as well as moral and ethical observances" (Hagins, Haden and Daly). As you can see, there are many different ways to define yoga. There are also many advantages families can gain from yoga.

Yoga has been shown to be beneficial for both adults and children. Since yoga has many different aspects to it, there are many different health benefits. According to Tanasi, et al., the physical practice of yoga improves flexibility, strengthens muscles, and releases tension. It also helps lower blood pressure and decrease heart rate. Since there is also a mental aspect of yoga, it has been shown that yoga helps people attain inner peace (Tanasi, Vishera and Newcomb).

Children reap specific benefits from yoga that are slightly different from what adults gain. According to Gillen and Gillen, children who have taken yoga classes have shown improvement in academic performance in school. Tanasi, et al., add that children who have taken yoga classes exhibit increased memory and mental processing speed. They also have a longer attention span. Gillen and Gillen also suggest that yoga helps children make healthier choices

Lastname 2

with regard to food options, and stress management. In my opinion, these are two very important traits for children's overall health and well-being.

According to Gillen and Gillen, one trait of yoga is stillness. Children often have difficulty being still; however, yoga helps children develop strategies to display stillness throughout their day. Once these strategies are perfected during a yoga session, the children can then use these techniques when their lives become chaotic. One moment of chaos that Gillen and Gillen use as an example is when children are packing up to go home at the end of a school day. Children who know how to be still can remain calm even when there are many children rushing around them. Furthermore, according to Tanasi, et al., yoga has been shown to lower levels of aggression in children, and to improve their ability to follow directions and cooperate in groups.

According to Tilak, children who take regular yoga classes have better self-esteem. The challenges of the poses in the physical practice of yoga help children see how strong their bodies are. When children see and can feel their strong bodies, they become more confident. For example, when doing a balance posture in a yoga class, children are encouraged to fall and get right back up to try again. Children are also encouraged to stay calm when they fall. When children finally master a balance pose they are having difficulty with, their self-esteem and confidence increase (Tilak).

In addition to the benefits mentioned above for all children, yoga has specific benefits for children with disabilities (Savita, Buckley-Reed and Alexander). According to Satvika, et al., yoga is often used in a behavior intervention plan for children with disabilities. Satvika et al., conducted a study in which 51 children with disabilities, ages 5 to 9, participated in 60 minutes of yoga every day first thing in the morning. The children in the study had disabilities such as autism spectrum disorder, multiple physical handicaps, and developmental disabilities. After 26

Lastname 3

weeks, the study found improved academic productivity, increased levels of independence and attention, and better self-regulation. Gillen and Gillen also found yoga to be beneficial for children with conditions such as attention deficit disorder (ADD) and attention deficit hyperactivity disorder (ADHD). As mentioned previously, Gillen and Gillen found that including moments of stillness in yoga practice encouraged children to use a moment of stillness when faced with chaos. Similarly, yoga teaches a child with ADD or ADHD to use moments of stillness to control their behavior. When these children use moments of stillness, they are able to focus and pay attention with more ease (Gillen and Gillen).

In my opinion, yoga is the perfect activity for families. As the research above states, the advantages of yoga for adults, children, and children with special needs are unique. It is my belief that all families who participate in yoga programs will benefit from these advantages.

Lastname 4

Works Cited

Gillen, L. and J. Gillen. *Yoga Calm for Children: Educating Heart, Mind, and Body.* Portland, OR: Three Pebbles Press, LLC., 2008.

Hagins, M., S. Haden and L. Daly. "A randomized controlled trial on the effects of yoga on stress reactivity in 6th grade students." *Evidence-Based Complementary and Alternative Medicine* 2013 (2013).

Satvika, G., et al. "The effectiveness of a manualized yoga intervention on classroom behaviors in elementary school children with disabilities: A pilot study." *Journal of Occupational Therapy, Schools, & Early Intervention* 6 (2013): 158-164.

Tanasi, A., et al. *Behavior management: Traditional and expanded approaches.* Landham, MD: University Press of America, Inc., 2013. 124-139.

Tilak, V. *The Benefits of Yoga for Kids.* n.d. 2013.
        <http://www.parents.com/fun/sports/exercise/the-benefits-of-yoga-for-kids/>.

# Word Review and Assessment

## Chapter 3 **Working with Tables and Objects**

### Study Quiz

*Online courseware includes a Study Quiz.*

### Features Review

*Online courseware includes a Features Review consisting of 10 multiple-choice questions to help reinforce your understanding of the chapter content.*

### Skills Review 1 **Using Table Formatting on a Visitors Log**

**Skills**    **CH1:** Use the Show/Hide ¶ feature, set margins, and insert headers and footers
**CH2:** Change font and font size, and use formatting tools **CH3:** Convert text to tables, change page orientation, insert and delete rows and columns in a table, and insert visual media

**Scenario**    You are the office receptionist for *Guidelines for Healthy Living Magazine.* Use table formatting to improve the appearance of a log that helps the magazine staff keep track of upcoming visitor appointments.

**Steps**

1. Open the student data file **C3R1-Visitors** and save the file as **C3R1-Visitors-Lastname**, but replace *Lastname* with your last name.

2. Change the page orientation to landscape and set the margins to the *Narrow* option.

3. Change the font of the title, *Today's Visitors Log,* to 18-point Calibri.

4. Convert the body of the document—the 16 lines of text below the title—to a table using the *AutoFit to contents* option with tabs separating the text. **Hint:** *Turn on Show/Hide ¶, select all 16 lines including the paragraph symbol at the end of each line, select* AutoFit to contents *in the Convert Text to Table dialog box, and ensure that* Tabs *is selected in the* Separate text at *section of the dialog box. Leave Show/Hide ¶ turned on for the remaining steps in this review.*

5. Adjust the right border of each column to the following specified inch marks on the ruler, ensure each column uses only one line per visitor. **Hint:** *Adjust the columns from right to left (starting with the column* To See *and ending with the column* Visitor's Name*).*

   | | |
   |---|---|
   | *To See* | 9 |
   | *AM/PM* | 8 |
   | *Time* | 7 |
   | *Email Address* | 6.0 |
   | *Cell Phone* | 3.5 |
   | *Visitor's Name* | 2 |

6   Apply bold formatting to all column headings.

7   Insert a row after the row that begins *Zachary Taylor* and type the following data in the appropriate columns: Millard Fillmore, 703.555.4455, mfillmore@ppi-edu.net, 2:00, PM, Jon. Proofread your entry. **Hint:** *To force the email address to appear as a hyperlink, press the Tab key after typing the email address.*

8   James Monroe has accidentally been entered twice in the same time slot. Delete the second row that begins *James Monroe*.

9   Peter Smith has canceled his appointment. Delete the row that begins *Peter Smith*.

10  On the first line of the document, insert the student data file **C3R1-Logo**, which is the *Guidelines for Healthy Living Magazine* logo. Press Enter two times to insert one blank line after the logo. Center the logo. **Hint:** *Use Show/Hide ¶ to be sure you insert the logo on the first line and insert exactly one blank line following the logo. After inserting the logo, click the picture and then click the Center button.*

11  Click to the left of the title *Today's Visitors Log*, and then use the Icons button in the Illustrations group on the Insert tab to insert the icon of the four adults in the *People* section shown in Completed Review 1.

12  Insert a header with your name on the left and the current date on the right.

13  Save the file.

14  Print or submit the completed file as directed by your instructor.

## *Completed Review 1*

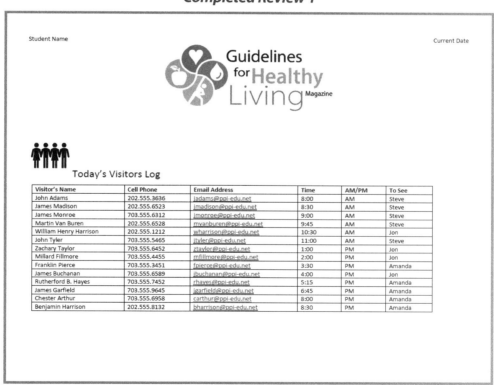

## Skills Review 2  **Using a Table to Create an Exercise Class Schedule**

**Skills**  **CH1:** Enter and edit text, use the Show/Hide ¶ feature, and insert headers and footers **CH2:** Change font and font size, and use formatting tools **CH3:** Create tables, merge rows or columns in a table, format tables, insert SmartArt, insert visual media, add alternative text, resize media, and align and format media

**Scenario**  You are the office manager for a busy local gym. Saturday classes are popular, and nobody wants to miss a favorite class. Create a schedule to let members know the time and location of all the Saturday exercise classes.

**Steps**

1  Open the student data file **C3R2-Schedule** and save the file as **C3R2-Schedule-Lastname**, but replace *Lastname* with your last name.

2  Change the font size of the title, *Exercise Class Schedule*, to 24 points and the font color to Green, Accent 6.

3  Change the font size of the subtitle, *Exercise Classes for Saturday*, to 16 points and the color to Blue, Accent 5.

4  Move the insertion point to the third blank line after the subtitle *Exercise Classes for Saturday* and then insert a table containing 5 columns and 15 rows. **Hint:** *Turn on Show/Hide ¶ to be sure you have exactly two blank lines (two paragraph marks) before the table.*

5  Type the values for the table cells as shown below. **Note:** *The italicized black numbers to the left of the table are for reference in Steps 6–11; do not type those numbers.*

| | |  |  |  |  |
|---|---|---|---|---|---|
| *1* | | Time | Gym | Studio | Spin Room |
| *2* | The gym opens at 8:00 AM on Saturday mornings. | | | | |
| *3* | Morning | 8:00 | | | |
| *4* | | 9:00 | | | Beginning Spin |
| *5* | | 10:00 | | | |
| *6* | | 11:00 | | Cardio Workout | |
| *7* | Afternoon | 12:00 | Muscle Maker | | Spin |
| *8* | | 1:00 | | Hip-hop | |
| *9* | | 2:00 | Trampoline Exercises | Step | |
| *10* | | 3:00 | | | Advanced Spin |
| *11* | | 4:00 | Fat Burn Workout | Shake It Off | |
| *12* | Evening | 5:00 | | | |
| *13* | | 6:00 | Kickboxing | Yoga | |
| *14* | | 7:00 | | Pilates | Spin |
| *15* | The gym closes at 8:00 PM on Saturday evenings. | | | | |

6   Apply bold formatting to row 1 in the table.

7   Merge all columns in row 2 so there is only one column in that row.

8   Merge all columns in row 15 so there is only one column in that row.

9   Merge the cells in rows 3–6 of the first column so there is only one row containing the word *Morning* for those cells.

10  Merge the cells in rows 7–11 of the first column so there is only one row containing the word *Afternoon* for those cells.

11  Merge the cells in rows 12–14 of the first column so there is only one row containing the word *Evening* for those cells.

12  Remove the outside border from the table.

13  Use the Online Pictures button in the Illustrations group on the Insert tab and type exercise in the search box to find an image similar to the one shown in Completed Review 2. Insert the image as shown in the completed skill, and then apply the following effects:
    a.  Change text wrapping to square.
    b.  Set the image height to 1.5 inches.
    c.  Move the image to align with the top of the title *Exercise Class Schedule* and with the right margin of the document.
    d.  Use the Color button in the Adjust group on the Picture Tools Format tab to recolor the image to Green, Accent color 6 Light.
    e.  Add the alternative text, An image showing an individual exercising.

14  Insert a header that includes your name at the left margin and the current date at the right margin.

15  At the end of the document, add a blank line so that two paragraph symbols appear after the table.

16  In the new blank line, insert the Equation SmartArt graphic. ***Hint:*** *Click the* Process *option in the left panel of the Choose a SmartArt Graphic dialog box and then scroll down in the middle panel to find the* Equation *option.*
    a.  Type the following text for the three bullet points in the graphic: Eat Right, Exercise, Feel Great!.
    b.  Change the colors of the graphic to Colorful Range - Accent Colors 4 to 5.
    c.  Add the alternative text, Eat right plus exercise equals feel great!.

17  Save the file.

18  Print or submit the completed file as directed by your instructor.

*Completed Review 2*

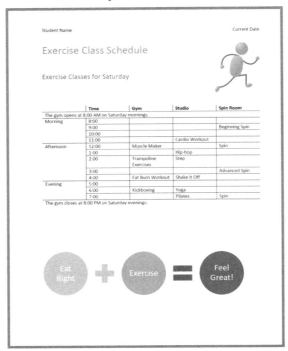

 ## Skills Review 3  **Creating an Attractive Newsletter**

**Skills**   **CH1:** Enter and edit text; use the Show/Hide ¶ feature; use cut, copy, and paste; indent and add tabs using the ruler; set margins; and insert headers and footers
**CH2:** Change font and font size, use formatting tools, align text, format paragraph and line spacing, create bulleted and numbered lists, and format text in columns
**CH3:** Change page orientation, insert visual media; add alternative text; resize media; and align and format media

**Scenario**   You have been asked to format the text for the annual *Guidelines for Healthy Living Magazine* newsletter in an attractive, three-column layout.

**Steps**

1  Open the student data file **C3R3-Food** and save the file as **C3R3-Food-Lastname**, but replace *Lastname* with your last name.

2  Change the orientation to landscape.

3  Set the margins to the *Narrow* option.

4  Insert a blank header, and then modify it as follows:
   a. Delete the placeholder.
   b. Insert the student data file **C3R3-Logo**, which is the *Guidelines for Healthy Living Magazine* logo. Set text wrapping to square.
   c. In the first line of the header, type Annual Newsletter, and then right-align the text. **Hint:** *Start by turning on Show/Hide ¶, and then place the insertion point before the first paragraph mark in the header. You may want to leave Show/Hide ¶ turned on for the remaining steps in this review.*
   d. Change the font effect of the text *Annual Newsletter* to small caps. **Hint:** *Select the text, click the dialog box launcher in the Font group on the Home tab to open the Font dialog box, click the* Small caps *check box to insert a check mark, and then click the OK button.*

     e. Change the font size of the text *Annual Newsletter* to 18 points and the font color to Light Blue.

     f. Delete any blank lines below the text *Annual Newsletter*.

5 Select the last line of text in the document (beginning *Adapted from the*), remove it and place it on the Clipboard, insert a footer in the document, and then paste the text from the Clipboard into the footer. **Hint:** *Select the last line of text, click the Cut button in the Clipboard group on the Home tab, insert a blank footer, and then click the Paste button.*

6 Center the footer text and apply italic formatting. Delete any blank lines below the footer text.

7 In the first line of the document, replace *Student Name* with your name and *Current Date* with today's date, right-align the text, and then insert three blank lines.

8 Select the body of the newsletter—from the line that begins *10 Tips for* through the line that ends *and tai chi.*—and complete these tasks:
     a. Change the line spacing to single and the spacing after paragraphs to 6 points.
     b. Create three columns of equal width.

9 Change the four bold headings (beginning *10 Tips for, How Activity and, The Importance of,* and *A Few Types*) to small caps and set the font color to Green, Accent 6. **Hint:** *Format the first heading and then use the Format Painter to copy the formatting to the remaining headings.*

10 Select the 10 tips—from the line that begins *Balance calories* through the line that begins *Drink water*—and apply the numbered list formatting. Use the Decrease Indent button in the Paragraph group on the Home tab to force the numbers to the left margin.

11 Insert a column page break to force the heading *A Few Types of Physical Activity* to appear at the top of the third column. **Hint:** *Place the insertion point in front of the heading, click the Layout tab, click the Breaks button in the Page Setup group, and then click the* Column *option in the drop-down list.*

12 Delete the blank line above the heading *The Importance of Physical Activity*.

13 Set the spacing before paragraphs to 12 points for the heading *The Importance of Physical Activity*.

14 Insert the student data file **C3R3-MyPlate**, which is the ChooseMyPlate.gov placemat image, in the section with the heading *How Activity and Nutrition Work Together*. **Hint:** *Place the insertion point at the end of the heading line and then insert the image.*
     a. Set text wrapping to tight.
     b. Adjust the width of the image to 1.5 inches.
     c. Place the image just below the heading, with the right margin of the image aligned with the right margin of the heading.
     d. Add the alternative text, Choosemyplate.gov logo.

15 Use the Shapes button to draw a 10-inch line between the magazine logo and the body of the newsletter, extending from the left margin to the right margin. Change the line color to black. **Hint:** *Hold down the Shift key to draw a straight line.*

16 Use the Shapes button to draw a rectangle enclosing the heading *How Activity and Nutrition Work Together* and the paragraph that follows it (beginning with *Physical activity* and ending with *eating less.*). Change the shape outline to Light Blue and the shape fill to No Fill.

17 Save the file.

18 Print or submit the completed file as directed by your instructor.

ANNUAL NEWSLETTER
Student Name Current Date

**10 TIPS FOR MAKING HEALTHY FOOD CHOICES**

1. Balance calories. Find out how many calories you need for a day as a first step in managing your weight. Being physically active also helps you balance calories.
2. Enjoy your food, but eat less. Eating too fast or when your attention is elsewhere may lead to eating too many calories. Pay attention to hunger and fullness cues before, during, and after meals.
3. Avoid oversized portions. Use a smaller plate, bowl, and glass. When eating out, choose a smaller size option, share a dish, or take home part of your meal.
4. Eat healthy foods more often. Eat more vegetables, fruits, whole grains, and fat-free or low-fat (1%) milk and dairy products.
5. Make half your plate fruits and vegetables.
6. Switch to fat-free or low-fat (1%) milk.
7. Make half your grains whole grains. Substitute a whole-grain product for a refined product—such as whole wheat bread instead of white bread or brown rice instead of white rice.
8. Eat less healthy foods less often. Cut back on foods high in solid fats, added sugars, and salt. Use these foods as occasional treats, not everyday foods.
9. Compare sodium in foods. Use the Nutrition Facts label to choose lower-sodium versions of foods.
10. Drink water instead of sugary drinks.

**HOW ACTIVITY AND NUTRITION WORK TOGETHER**

Physical activity and nutrition work together for better health. Being active increases the amount of calories burned.  As people age, their metabolism slows, so maintaining energy balance requires moving more and eating less.

**THE IMPORTANCE OF PHYSICAL ACTIVITY**

Regular physical activity can produce long-term health benefits. People of all ages, shapes, sizes, and abilities can benefit from being physically active. The more physically active you are, the greater the health benefits.

**A FEW TYPES OF PHYSICAL ACTIVITY**

*Aerobic activities* make you breathe harder and make your heart beat faster. Aerobic activities can be moderate or vigorous in their intensity. Vigorous activities take more effort than moderate ones. For moderate activities, you can talk while you do them, but you can't sing. For vigorous activities, you can only say a few words without stopping to catch your breath.

*Muscle-strengthening activities* make your muscles stronger. These include push-ups and weight lifting. It is important to work all the different parts of the body—legs, hips, back, chest, stomach, shoulders, and arms.

*Bone-strengthening activities* make your bones stronger. These activities produce a force on the bones that promotes growth and strength.

*Balance and stretching activities* enhance physical stability and flexibility, which reduces risk of injuries. Examples are gentle stretching, dancing, yoga, martial arts, and tai chi.

*Adapted from the USDA Center for Nutrition Policy and Promotion's ChooseMyPlate.gov website.*

# Word Review and Assessment

## Chapter 4 **Finalizing and Sharing Documents**

### Study Quiz

*Online courseware includes a Study Quiz.*

### Features Review

*Online courseware includes a Features Review consisting of 10 multiple-choice questions to help reinforce your understanding of the chapter content.*

### Skills Review 1 **Editing an Audio Recording Script**

**Skills**    **CH1:** Enter and edit text, and insert headers and footers **CH2:** Apply styles **CH4:** Turn on and view Track Changes, and make changes and add comments

**Scenario**    The story of Goldilocks and the three bears has entertained children for more than a century. You volunteer for a nonprofit organization that creates audio recordings of children's stories, and you have been asked to help correct mistakes in the script for a recording of this story. Use Track Changes in the Tracking group on the Review tab to correct the original document, and add a comment identifying the original source of the story.

**Steps**

1   Open the student data file named **C4R1-Goldilocks** and save it as **C4R1-Goldilocks-Lastname**, but replace *Lastname* with your last name.

2   Turn on Track Changes and set the *Display for Review* option box to All Markup.

3   Change the style for the first line, *Goldilocks and the Three Bears*, to Title.

4   In the title, select the words *Three Bears* and insert a comment, typing the following as the comment text: Original fairy tale recorded by Robert Southey in 1837.

5   Insert a header with your name on the left and the current date on the right.

6   Insert a footer with a plain page number centered on the page.

7   With Track Changes still turned on, make the following corrections:
   a. In the first paragraph, which begins *Once upon a*, change *Golden Locks* to Goldilocks.
   b. In the second paragraph, which begins *At the table*, change *pudding* to porridge.
   c. In the third paragraph, which begins *"This porridge is too hot!*, change *examined* to exclaimed.
   d. In the seventh paragraph, which begins *"Oh my, this*, change *Oh my* to Ahhh.
   e. In the 14th paragraph, which begins *Goldilocks was very*, insert the word first before the word *bed* in the second sentence, so the sentence reads *She lay down in the first bed, but it was too hard*.
   f. Also in the 14th paragraph, delete the second-to-last word, *fast*.
   g. In the 22nd paragraph, which begins *They decided to*, change *Father* to Papa.
   h. In the 25th paragraph, which begins *Just then, Goldilocks* change *Cute* to Help.

8   Save the document.

9   Print or submit the completed file as directed by your instructor.

*Completed Review 1*

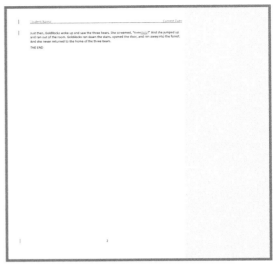

 ## Skills Review 2  **Revising a Poorly Edited Nursery Rhyme**

**Skills**    **CH1:** Enter and edit text, use the Show/Hide ¶ feature, and insert headers and footers
**CH4:** Turn on and view Track Changes, accept or reject changes and review comments, and send a document for editing via email

**Scenario**    "One, two…" is a nursery rhyme that is a favorite among children. They have fun reciting the words while learning about rhymes and counting. An editor reviewed a version of "One, two…" and made changes to fix problems found in it. Unfortunately, the editor's suggestions are not all correct. The original version is shown in Completed Review 2. Compare the words in the original version with the edited version. Accept or reject the editor's changes as necessary to make the edited version match the original version. After acting on the comments, delete them. Do not make any other changes to the text.

**Steps**

1  Open the student data file named **C4R2-NRhyme** and save it as **C4R2-NRhyme-Lastname**, but replace *Lastname* with your last name.

2  Turn off the Track Changes feature and set the *Display for Review* option box to All Markup.

3  Insert a header with your name on the left and the current date on the right.

4  In the document body, accept or reject the changes as instructed below, so that the document matches Completed Review 2.
   a. Accept the format change for the title, *"One, two…"* .
   b. Accept the format change for the author line, *by Mother Goose.*
   c. Accept the blank line inserted under the author line. ***Hint:*** *Turn on Show/Hide ¶ to see the paragraph mark.*
   d. Reject the change of *six* to *seven.*
   e. Accept the change of *even* to *straight.*
   f. Read and then delete the comment related to the word *delve.*
   g. Reject the change of *Maids* to *Queens.*

**5** Save the document.

**6** Send the document to your instructor by sending it as an email attachment. Edit the Subject to read Nursery Rhyme. Type the following message in the body of the email: Please review the attached document and let me know if you have edits. ***Note:*** *Your instructor may provide different instructions for submission.*

### Completed Review 2

---

## Skills Review 3  **Finalizing and Sharing a Memo**

**Skills**   **CH1:** Enter and edit text **CH2:** Change font and font size **CH4:** Share a file for editing and create a PDF file

**Scenario**   You are the administrative assistant for the nonprofit organization Audio Access to Children's Literature. The office manager has asked you to finalize a memo about a planned phone system upgrade and then send it to the editorial director and production manager. Make the requested changes to the memo, create a PDF file, and then send the file as an email attachment or share it on OneDrive.

**Steps**

**1** Open the student data file named **C4R3-Phone** and save it as **C4R3-Phone-Lastname**, but replace *Lastname* with your last name.

**2** Replace the words *Student Name* with your name and the words *Current Date* with the current date (*March 7, 2021* format).

**3** Format the word *Memo* so it is right-aligned and 48-point Script MT Bold.

**4** Save the document without closing it.

**5** Resave the document as a PDF file. Use the same name as your Word document: **C4R3-Phone-Lastname**.

**6** Use the Share button to share the document with your instructor. ***Note:*** *You will be prompted to save the document to OneDrive if the document is currently saved to a different storage medium.* Include the message Please review the attached document.

*Completed Review 3*

# Memo

To:     John Smith
        Sasha Janish

From:   Student Name

Cc:     Pamen Loosh

Date:   Current Date

Re:     Phone System Upgrade

---

Meeting called by Jane Doe, CFO.

Please mark your schedule to attend a meeting on Wed March 14 at 2:00 PM in Conference Room A to discuss the possibility of a phone system upgrade for employees working in our St. Paul, MN office. Our current phone system is approximately 10 years old. An updated phone system will provide VoIP features, audio conferencing, and an automated phone directory.

Please respond with your intention to attend.

# Word Review and Assessment

## Unit **4 Microsoft Word**

### Skills Assessment 1 **"Ergonomically Correct" Handout**

**Skills** **CH1:** Enter and edit text; use the Show/Hide ¶ feature; use cut, copy, and paste; set margins; insert a page break; and insert headers and footers **CH2:** Insert citations, create a Works Cited page, change font and font size, use formatting tools, apply styles, align text, create bulleted and numbered lists, format text in columns, and copy formatting with Format Painter **CH3:** Insert visual media, add alternative text, resize media, and align and format media **CH4:** Share a file for editing, and create a PDF file

**Scenario** You work part-time in the media center at your school, and you know that most students spend a lot of time at the computer. You have recently become aware that extended computer use can place a huge strain on the body. You prepare a handout about creating an ergonomically appropriate environment to share with students who visit the media center. You add formatting to the handout to make it attractive and easy to read.

**Steps**

1 Open the student data file named **U4A1-Ergonomics** and save it as **U4A1-Ergonomics-Lastname**, but replace *Lastname* with your last name.

2 Insert a header with your name on the left and the current date on the right.

3 Apply the Heading 1 style to the title, *Reduce the Strain! Cut the Pain!* Change the font size to 26 points and apply bold formatting.

4 Apply the Heading 2 style to the subtitle, *Create an Ergonomically Appropriate Environment*. Apply italic formatting.

5 Apply the Subtle Reference style to the headings *What Is Ergonomics?* and *Ergonomic Tips for Computer Users*. Change the font size to 14 points and apply bold formatting.

6 Apply the Subtle Reference style to the four tip headings: *Working Area, Posture, Breaks,* and *Keyboarding*. Apply bold formatting to each tip heading. **Hint:** *Change the format for the first tip heading, and then use Format Painter to copy the formatting to the other three tip headings.*

7 Move the "Breaks" section—which begins with the line *Breaks* and ends with the blank line below the line beginning *Give your eyes*—above the "Posture" section. Check to be sure there is one blank line above each of the tips headings (*Working Area, Breaks, Posture,* and *Keyboarding*). Add or delete blank lines as needed. **Hint:** *Turn on Show/Hide ¶. Cut the "Breaks" section, including the paragraph mark below the last line of text; place the insertion point at the beginning of the* Posture *heading; and then paste the "Breaks" section. Leave Show/Hide ¶ turned on for the remaining steps in this assessment.*

8 Apply the Narrow margin setting to the entire document.

9 Change the layout for the "Ergonomic Tips for Computer Users" section to two-column. **Hint:** *Select the text beginning with the heading* Working Area *and ending with the paragraph mark at the end of the line beginning* Do not use.

10 Place check-mark bullets in front of the tips in each of the four tip sections. Do not bullet the tip headings.

11 Delete the blank lines above the tip headings *Working Area, Breaks, Posture,* and *Keyboarding*. These section separators are no longer needed. **Hint:** *Use Show/Hide ¶ to find the paragraph marks for these blank lines.*

12. Delete the blank line above the last line of text, which begins *Work comfortably!*

13. Select the last line of text, which begins *Work comfortably!*, apply the Heading 1 style, and center the text.

14. Place the insertion point at the end of the heading *What Is Ergonomics?* Use the Online Pictures tool, with the search phrase ergonomics, to find and insert the graphic shown in Completed Assessment 1 or a similar image. If you cannot find the exact image shown, select another appropriate graphic. Add appropriate alternative text to the image.

15. Change the width of the image to 2.6 inches, height to 2.07 inches, and the text wrapping to *Square*. **Hint:** *Use the Picture Tools Format tab.*

16. Drag the image to position it to the right of the "What Is Ergonomics?" section, aligning the top of the image with the top of the section heading and the right edge of the image with the right margin of the document, as shown in Completed Assessment 1.

17. Set the citation style to *MLA,* and then click at the end of the last bulleted item under the *Keyboarding* tips heading. Insert a citation using the following information:

| | |
|---|---|
| *Type of Source* | Web site |
| *Name of Web Page* | Office ergonomics: Your how-to guide |
| *Name of Web Site* | Mayo Clinic |
| *Year* | 2016 |
| *Month* | April |
| *Day* | 20 |
| *URL* | https://www.mayoclinic.org |

18. Click at the end of the last line of text (the line beginning *Work Comfortably!*) and insert a page break.

19. Press the Enter key and then insert a Works Cited page.

20. Save the document.

21. Resave the document as a PDF file. Use the same name as your Word document: **U4A1-Ergonomics-Lastname**.

22. Share the PDF file with your instructor by sending it as an email attachment or by posting and sharing it on OneDrive. **Note:** *Your instructor may provide different instructions for submission.*

*Completed Assessment 1*

## Skills Assessment 2  Fitness Equipment Order Confirmation

**Skills**     **CH1:** Enter and edit text, and use the Show/Hide ¶ feature **CH2:** Change font and font size, use formatting tools, apply styles, align text, and format paragraph and line spacing **CH3:** Create tables and format tables

**Scenario**  You are the sales manager for a company that sells fitness equipment. Last week, you met with a client and evaluated the client's need for new equipment. Create and format a letter that confirms the potential equipment order.

**Steps**

1   Open the student data file named **U4A2-Equipment** and save it as **U4A2-Equipment-Lastname**, but replace *Lastname* with your last name.

2   In the fifth line of the letter, replace the words *Current Date* with the current date, and in the closing, replace the words *Student Name* with your name.

3   Change the font for the entire document to 12-point Calibri.

4   In the first line, apply the Heading 1 style to the company name, *Fitness Providers, Inc.*

5   Modify the two lines containing Fitness Providers' contact information (address and phone number) as follows:
    a.  Place the street address on the same line as the city, state, and zip code, separated by a comma and a single space. You now have two lines with company contact information, with the second line containing just the phone number.
    b.  Apply the Subtitle style to the two lines of contact information.
    c.  Single-space the two lines and set the spacing after paragraphs to 0.

6   Center the company name and contact information.

7   Single-space the recipient's address—beginning with the line *Ms. Sophia Treaders* and ending with the line *New York, NY 10003*—and set the spacing after paragraphs to 0.

8   Remove the blank lines after the salutation (*Dear Ms. Sophia Treaders:*) and after the two paragraphs ending with *memberships:* and *quote.* **Hint:** *Turn on Show/Hide ¶ and delete the appropriate paragraph marks.*

9   In the closing, add two blank lines above your name, so that there are three paragraph symbols between the line *Thank you,* and the line with your name.

10  Single-space the closing, from the line with your name through the line *Sales Representative*, and set the spacing after paragraphs to 0.

11  Also in the closing, italicize your title, *Sales Representative.*

12  Add a table after the paragraph that ends with *growth in memberships:* and before the paragraph beginning *If you agree*, as follows:
    a.  Insert a table that has 2 columns and 8 rows.
    b.  In row 1, type and format column headings as follows:
        i   Left column: type Equipment, apply bold formatting, and align center left (vertical center and horizontal left)
        ii  Right column: type Quantity, apply bold formatting, and align center (vertical and horizontal center)
    c.  In rows 2–8, type the following equipment names and quantities:

        Treadmills             3
        Bicycles               2
        Elliptical machines    4
        Rowing machine         1
        Leg press machine      1
        Mats                   5
        Yoga balls             5

    d. Center the data in the *Quantity* column.

    e. Change the font color of the column headings to Green.

    f. Size the columns to fit the contents using the AutoFit button on the Table Tools Layout tab.

    g. Click the table move handle and then center the table using the Center button on the Home tab.

    h. Remove all table borders.

**13** Click in the paragraph below the table and set the spacing before paragraphs to 12 points.

**14** Save the document.

**15** Print or submit the file as directed by your instructor.

### *Completed Assessment 2*

Fitness Providers, Inc.
123 Fifth Street, St. Louis Park, MN 55416
800-123-4567

Current Date

Ms. Sophia Treaders
Sophia's Fitness Center
2345 Broadway
New York, NY 10003

Dear Ms. Sophia Treaders:

Thank you for your interest in purchasing exercise equipment from Fitness Providers, Inc. Based on the discussion at our meeting last week, I am proposing you add the following equipment to support your anticipated growth in memberships:

| Equipment | Quantity |
| --- | --- |
| Treadmills | 3 |
| Bicycles | 2 |
| Elliptical machines | 4 |
| Rowing machine | 1 |
| Leg press machine | 1 |
| Mats | 5 |
| Yoga balls | 5 |

If you agree that these quantities are appropriate, I will follow-up with a price quote.

Thank you,

Student Name
*Sales Representative*

## Skills Assessment 3  Upcoming Event Flyer

**Skills**   **CH1:** Enter and edit text, and perform a spelling and grammar check **CH2:** Change font and font size, use formatting tools, apply styles, align text, and format paragraph and line spacing **CH3:** Insert SmartArt, insert media, resize media, and align and format media **CH4:** Turn on and view Track Changes, make changes and add comments, accept or reject changes and review comments, send a document for editing via email, share a file for editing, and create a PDF file ***Note:*** *The skills list may vary depending on choices made by the student.*

**Scenario**   You are in charge of promoting an upcoming event at your school. Work with a partner to come up with a creative idea for an event. Then, you and your partner will each create a flyer promoting the event. Be sure to include all relevant information, such as the date, time, cost, and so forth. The flyer should fill one page completely, without continuing onto a second page. When you are finished, share the flyer with your partner and use the Track Changes to edit each other's flyers. When your flyer is edited and complete, save it in both Word and PDF formats.

### Steps, Part A

Your instructor will pair you with another student. Brainstorm to come up with a creative idea for an event. You may want to refer to the school calendar for ideas.

### Steps, Part B

blank

Start with a new, blank Word document or a flyer template. The flyer you create must include the following information:

> Title of the event
> Event date
> Event time
> Event location
> Event location address
> Price of tickets (if applicable)
> A short description of the event
> At least one image or logo

Use at least five different formatting techniques and fill one page completely, without going over onto a second page. The flyer should be informative and attractive. Save the Word document and the PDF with the same name: **U4A3-B-Flyer-Lastname**.

### Steps, Part C

When you have finished your flyer, turn on Track Changes and share the document with your partner using email or the Share feature. When you receive your partner's flyer, edit it. The reviewed document must contain at least two modifications to text, at least one modification to format, and at least two comments. Save the reviewed document as **U4A3-C-Flyer** and then use email or the Share feature to send it back.

### Steps, Part D

After your partner returns the flyer you created, read the comments and look over the tracked changes. Make decisions about the suggested changes by using the Accept or Reject buttons on the Review tab. Delete the comments. After you complete the review, check the document for spelling errors and correct any that you find. Ensure that the formatting makes the appropriate sections stand out and that the content fits on one page only. Save the completed document using the file name **U4A3-D-Flyer-Lastname**. Create a PDF version of the flyer. Save the PDF with the same name: **U4A3-D-Flyer-Lastname**.

### Steps, Part E

Share the file with your instructor.

Word Review and Assessment

# UNIT 5

# Excel Review and Assessment

Chapter 1    **Creating an Excel Workbook**

Chapter 2    **Working with Formulas and Functions**

Chapter 3    **Formatting Cells**

Chapter 4    **Working with Charts**

**Unit 5 Skills Assessment**

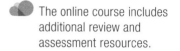 The online course includes additional review and assessment resources.

# Excel Review and Assessment

## Chapter 1 Creating an Excel Workbook

### Study Quiz

*Online courseware includes a Study Quiz.*

### Features Review

*Online courseware includes a Features Review consisting of 10 multiple-choice questions to help reinforce your understanding of the chapter content.*

### Skills Review 1 **Setting Up a Weekly Schedule**

**Skills**    **CH1:** Understand worksheet and workbook structure; use cell references; enter text, values, and dates; use the Auto Fill feature; insert and delete columns and rows; add, rename, move, and delete worksheets; insert headers and footers; and explore options for printing

**Scenario**   You have just started a part-time job, and you need to let your employer know your availability. Create a new workbook and enter your school schedule in a format that is easy to understand.

**Steps**

1 Create a new, blank workbook file.

2 Save the file as **C1R1-Schedule-Lastname**, but replace *Lastname* with your last name.

3 Type Weekly Schedule in cell A1.

4 Type your name in cell A2.

5 Type the current date in cell C2.

6 Type the following entries in cells A4:B4.
Hour
Monday

7 Type the following entries in cells A5:A6. ***Note:*** *Excel automatically changes* am *to* AM.
9 am
11 am

8 Type the following entries in cells B5:B8.
Sociology
Computer Applications
Accounting
Sports Marketing

9 Drag to select cells A5:A6 and then double-click the fill handle to fill the Hour entry series.

10 Make cell B4 active and then drag the fill handle to enter the days of the week *Tuesday* through *Friday* in cells C4:F4.

11 Drag to select cells B5:B8 and then use Auto Fill to copy Monday's schedule to Tuesday through Friday.

12 Rename the current sheet, typing Schedule as the new name.

13 Insert a new row 7.

**14** Type the following entries in cells A7:B7.
12:30 pm
Lunch

**15** Use Auto Fill to copy the Lunch entry to cells C7:F7.

**16** Change the width of columns B through F to fit the contents.

**17** Add print gridlines.

**18** Add a header with the sheet name and a footer with the page number.

**19** Click the File tab and then click the *Print* option to see how the file will look when printed.

**20** Change the print orientation to landscape.

**21** Save the workbook file.

**22** Print or submit the completed file as directed by your instructor.

*Completed Review 1, Step 20*

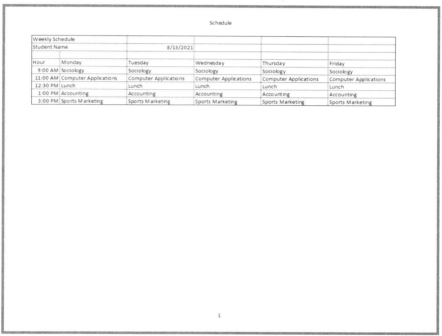

## Skills Review 2  **Making a Healthy Pizza on a Budget**

**Skills**  **CH1:** Understand worksheet and workbook structure; use cell references; enter text, values, and dates; use the Auto Fill feature; add, rename, move, and delete worksheets; insert headers and footers; and explore options for printing

**Scenario** Pizza is one of your favorite foods, but you are on a strict budget and trying to eat healthy. You wonder whether you could save money—and eat better—by making pizza instead of buying it. Create an Excel worksheet that displays the cost of making different types of healthy pizzas.

**Steps**

**1** Create a new, blank workbook file.

**2** Save the file as **C1R2-Pizza-Lastname**, but replace *Lastname* with your last name.

**3** Type Healthy Pizza on a Budget in cell A1.

**4** Type your name in cell A2.

**5** Type the following entries in cells A4:A8.
Ingredients
Whole wheat dough
Turkey pepperoni
Part-skim mozzarella
Green peppers

**6** Type the following entries in cells B4:E4.
Everything
Pepperoni
Vegetarian
Cheese

**7** Type the following entries in cells B5:B8. Be sure to type the numbers exactly as shown, including the dollar sign and trailing zeros.
$1.50
$2.00
$3.50
$1.25

**8** Select the range B5:B8 and copy the values across the rows through column E.

**9** Replace the entry in cell E7, typing the new entry as $4.50.

**10** Delete the entries in cells D6:E6.

**11** Delete the entry in cell E8.

**12** Resize columns A through E to fit the longest entry in its entirety.

**13** Change the print orientation to landscape.

**14** Rename the current worksheet, typing Pizza as the new name.

**15** Add a header and then insert the sheet name in the header.

**16** Save the workbook file.

**17** Print or submit the completed file as directed by your instructor.

### Completed Review 2

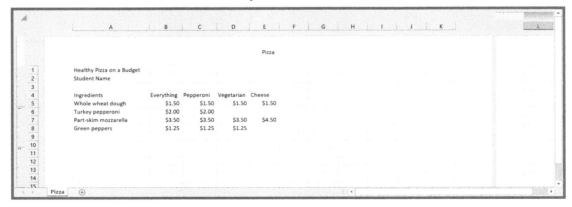

## Skills Review 3 Comparing Calories

**Skills**  **CH1:** Understand worksheet and workbook structure; use cell references; enter text, values, and dates; use the Auto Fill feature; use the spelling checker; and add, rename, move, and delete worksheets

**Scenario**  You know vegetables are healthy, but you've also heard that some have more calories than others. Create a workbook file for comparing the amount of calories in your favorite vegetables.

**Steps**

1  Create a new, blank workbook file.

2  Save the file as **C1R3-Vegetables-Lastname**, but replace *Lastname* with your last name.

3  Type Calory Compareson in cell A1. (Type exactly as written here. You will correct typos later.)

4  Type your name in cell A2.

5  Type Vegetable in cell A4, Measure in cell B4, and Calories in cell C4.

6  Type the following entries in cells A5:A9.
Green peas
Carrots
Cauliflower
Kale
Edamame

7  Type 1/2 cup, for the first measure, in cell B5.

8  Use Auto Fill to copy the measure from cell B5 to cells B6 through B9.

9  Type the following entries in cells C5:C9.
59
25
15
19
100

10  Check spelling in the worksheet, fixing any errors.

11  Rename the current sheet, typing Calorie Comparison as the new name.

12  Change the size of column A so that all entries fit in the column.

13  Save the workbook file.

14  Print or submit the completed workbook file as directed by your instructor.

### Completed Review 3

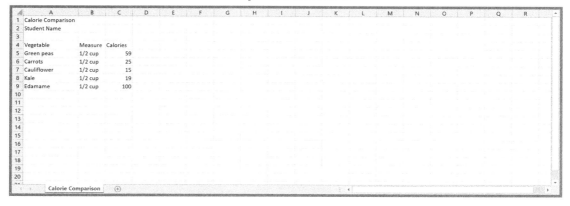

# Excel Review and Assessment

## Chapter 2 **Working with Formulas and Functions**

### Study Quiz

*Online courseware includes a Study Quiz.*

### Features Review

*Online courseware includes a Features Review consisting of 10 multiple-choice questions to help reinforce your understanding of the chapter content.*

### Skills Review 1 **Creating a GPA Calculator**

**Skills**    **CH1:** Enter text, values, and dates **CH2:** Enter a formula, enter a function, use AutoSum, use absolute and relative cell references, copy and move cell contents, sort data, and filter data

**Scenario**    You need to maintain a 3.00 GPA to keep your scholarship. To make sure you are achieving this goal, you create a spreadsheet to track your GPA.

**Steps**

1. Open the student data file named **C2R1-GPA**. Save the file as **C2R1-GPA-Lastname**, but replace *Lastname* with your last name.

2. Type your name in cell B3.

3. Type 85776 as your student ID in cell E3.

4. In cell D6, enter a formula that uses an absolute reference to calculate the points you earn for a course awarded the letter grade A. ***Hint:*** *Multiply the number of credits the course is worth (in cell B6) by the number of points awarded for the letter grade A (in cell I4).*

5. Copy the formula from cell D6 down the column for each course that received the same letter grade, A.

6. In cell D9, enter a formula that uses an absolute reference to calculate the points you earn for a course awarded the letter grade B+.

7. Copy the formula from cell D9 down the column for each course that received a letter grade of B+.

8. In cell D11, enter a formula that uses an absolute reference to calculate the points you earn for a course awarded the letter grade B.

9. Copy the formula from cell D11 down the column for each course that received a letter grade of B.

10. In cell B14, use AutoSum to create a formula that calculates the total credits.

11. In cell D14, use a function to create a formula that calculates the total points.

12. In cell D16, enter a formula that calculates the GPA. ***Hint:*** *Divide the total number of points awarded by the total number of credits earned.*

13. Select the range A6:D13 and then sort the selected range by the Courses column in ascending order.

14. Select the range A5:D13 and then filter the selected range to display only courses that achieved a letter grade of A.

15. Remove the filter.

**16** Save the worksheet file.

**17** Print or submit the completed file as directed by your instructor.

*Note: The VLOOKUP() function could be used as an alternative to the formulas you entered in column D. Refer to Excel Help for more information about the VLOOKUP() function. Check with your instructor before substituting VLOOKUP() in your worksheet for this exercise.*

### Completed Review 1

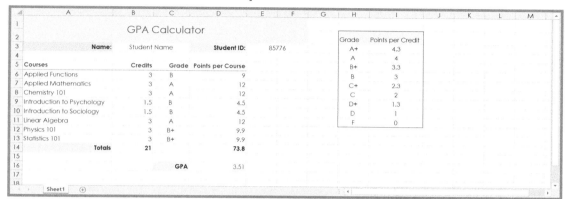

## Skills Review 2 **Completing an Invoice**

**Skills**   **CH1:** Enter text, values, and dates; and add, rename, move, and delete worksheets
**CH2:** Enter a formula, enter a function, insert a function, use AutoSum, use absolute and relative cell references, copy and move cell contents, and edit cell contents

**Scenario**   You sell security products for Endpoint, Inc. You need an invoice that totals the amount due for each item purchased based on the quantity, calculates and adds tax, and then calculates the amount of tax and invoice totals. You also need a blank version of the worksheet to use as a starting point for additional invoices.

**Steps**

**1** Open the student data file named **C2R2-Invoice**. Save the file as **C2R2-Invoice-Lastname**, but replace *Lastname* with your last name.

**2** Type your name in cell A3.

**3** Change invoice number (cell B4) to *1010*.

**4** In cell E4, insert a function to display the current date. Resize column E to fit the length of its longest entry.

**5** In cell D8, enter a formula that calculates the cost amount for the quantity purchased. Do not use a function. Copy the formula through row 13. **Hint:** *Multiply the quantity times the rate.*

**6** In cell E8, enter a formula that calculates the tax due using an absolute reference that refers to the tax rate in cell B5. Do not use a function. Copy the formula through row 13. **Hint:** *Multiply the amount times the tax rate.*

**7** In cell F8, enter a formula that adds the amount and tax for the quantity purchased. Do not use a function. Copy the formula through row 13.

**8** In cell E15, use a function to create a formula that calculates the total amount of tax for this order. The total should include rows 8 through 13 so that the total will automatically recalculate correctly if additional items are added to the invoice in rows 12 and 13.

9   In cell F17, use a function that calculates the invoice total for cells F8 through F13.

10  Change the badge quantity to *60*.

11  Add a new sheet, Sheet2, to the workbook.

12  Select the range A1:F17 on Sheet 1, copy it, and then paste it to the same range on Sheet2. Use the Paste Options button to keep the original column widths.

13  On Sheet2, clear the contents from cells B4, E4, and A8:C11 to prepare a blank invoice.

14  Rename Sheet2, typing Invoice # as its new name, and rename Sheet1, typing Invoice 1010 as its new name.

15  Save the workbook file.

16  Print or submit the completed file as directed by your instructor.

### Completed Review 2, Invoice 1010 Sheet

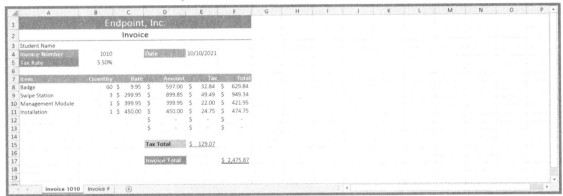

### Completed Review 2, Invoice # Sheet

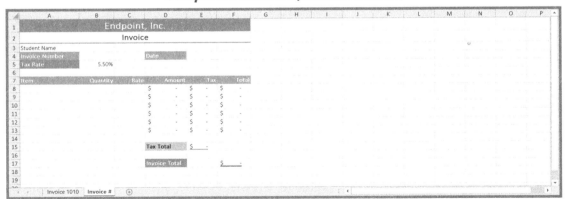

## Skills Review 3 **Calculating Your Utility Budget**

**Skills**    **CH1:** Enter text, values, and dates **CH2:** Enter a formula, enter a function, insert a function, use AutoSum, use absolute and relative cell references, copy and move cell contents, sort data, and use Show Formulas

**Scenario**    Your monthly utility bill includes fixed costs (costs that are the same each month) for your mobile phone and water/sewer. It also includes variable costs (costs that are different each month) for your electricity and natural gas. Your fixed costs are projected to increase next year. You want to track your monthly utility bills and use that data to create a projected budget for next year. Complete the budget and review its formulas.

**Steps**

1   Open the student data file named **C2R3-UtilBudget**. Save the file as **C2R3-UtilBudget-Lastname**, but replace *Lastname* with your last name.

2   Make the Current Year sheet active and then type your name in cell A2.

3   In row 9, use AutoSum and the fill handle to calculate the monthly totals for January through December.

4   In the range N5:P8, use functions to find the *Total*, *Average*, and *Max* values for each type of utility. In cell N9, calculate the grand total for all utilities.

5   Copy the range A1:P9 and paste it to the same range on the Projected sheet. Use the Paste Options button to keep the source column widths.

*Complete Steps 6–13 on the Projected sheet.*

6   Change the entry in cell A3 to *Projected*.

7   Water/Sewer values are projected to increase by 5% next year. In cell C14, type 5%.

8   Mobile Phone values are projected to increase by 3% next year. In cell C15, type 3%.

9   In cell B8, replace the existing content with a formula that calculates the projected Water/Sewer value. Use absolute cell references and parentheses where required. **Hint:** *The projected value is calculated by multiplying the previous year's value by the projected increase and then adding the previous year's value to the result.*

10   Copy the formula in cell B8 to the appropriate monthly cells in row 8.

11   In cell B5, enter a formula that calculates the projected Mobile Phone value. Use absolute references and parentheses where required. **Hint:** *The projected value is calculated by multiplying the previous year's value by the projected increase and then adding the previous year's value to the result.*

12   Copy the formula in cell B5 to the appropriate monthly cells in row 5.

13   Select the range A5:P8 and then sort the selected range based on the Utility column in ascending order.

14   Use Show Formulas to verify that you used absolute references and parentheses correctly in rows 5 and 8.

15   Save the workbook file.

16   Print or submit the completed file as directed by your instructor.

## Completed Review 3, Current Year Sheet

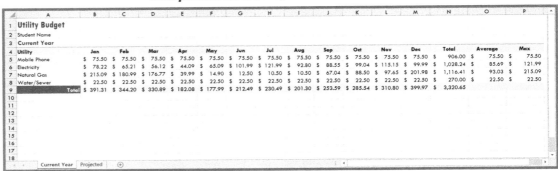

| Utility | Jan | Feb | Mar | Apr | May | Jun | Jul | Aug | Sep | Oct | Nov | Dec | Total | Average | Max |
|---|---|---|---|---|---|---|---|---|---|---|---|---|---|---|---|
| **Utility Budget** | | | | | | | | | | | | | | | |
| Student Name | | | | | | | | | | | | | | | |
| Current Year | | | | | | | | | | | | | | | |
| Mobile Phone | $ 75.50 | $ 75.50 | $ 75.50 | $ 75.50 | $ 75.50 | $ 75.50 | $ 75.50 | $ 75.50 | $ 75.50 | $ 75.50 | $ 75.50 | $ 75.50 | 906.00 | $ 75.50 | $ 75.50 |
| Electricity | $ 78.22 | $ 65.21 | $ 56.12 | $ 44.09 | $ 65.09 | $ 101.99 | $ 121.99 | $ 92.80 | $ 88.55 | $ 99.04 | $ 115.15 | $ 99.99 | 1,028.24 | $ 85.69 | $ 121.99 |
| Natural Gas | $ 215.09 | $ 180.99 | $ 176.77 | $ 39.99 | $ 14.90 | $ 12.50 | $ 10.50 | $ 10.50 | $ 67.04 | $ 88.50 | $ 97.65 | $ 201.98 | 1,116.41 | $ 93.03 | $ 215.09 |
| Water/Sewer | $ 22.50 | $ 22.50 | $ 22.50 | $ 22.50 | $ 22.50 | $ 22.50 | $ 22.50 | $ 22.50 | $ 22.50 | $ 22.50 | $ 22.50 | $ 22.50 | 270.00 | $ 22.50 | $ 22.50 |
| Total | $ 391.31 | $ 344.20 | $ 330.89 | $ 182.08 | $ 177.99 | $ 212.49 | $ 230.49 | $ 201.30 | $ 253.59 | $ 285.54 | $ 310.80 | $ 399.97 | 3,320.65 | | |

Current Year | Projected

## Completed Review 3, Projected Sheet, Step 13

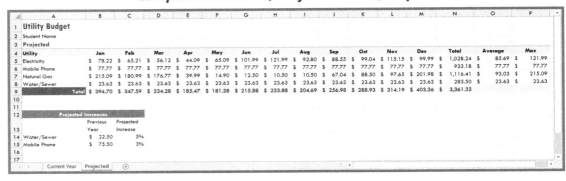

| Utility | Jan | Feb | Mar | Apr | May | Jun | Jul | Aug | Sep | Oct | Nov | Dec | Total | Average | Max |
|---|---|---|---|---|---|---|---|---|---|---|---|---|---|---|---|
| **Utility Budget** | | | | | | | | | | | | | | | |
| Student Name | | | | | | | | | | | | | | | |
| Projected | | | | | | | | | | | | | | | |
| Electricity | $ 78.22 | $ 65.21 | $ 56.12 | $ 44.09 | $ 65.09 | $ 101.99 | $ 121.99 | $ 92.80 | $ 88.55 | $ 99.04 | $ 115.15 | $ 99.99 | 1,028.24 | $ 85.69 | $ 121.99 |
| Mobile Phone | $ 77.77 | $ 77.77 | $ 77.77 | $ 77.77 | $ 77.77 | $ 77.77 | $ 77.77 | $ 77.77 | $ 77.77 | $ 77.77 | $ 77.77 | $ 77.77 | 933.18 | $ 77.77 | $ 77.77 |
| Natural Gas | $ 215.09 | $ 180.99 | $ 176.77 | $ 39.99 | $ 14.90 | $ 12.50 | $ 10.50 | $ 10.50 | $ 67.04 | $ 88.50 | $ 97.65 | $ 201.98 | 1,116.41 | $ 93.03 | $ 215.09 |
| Water/Sewer | $ 23.63 | $ 23.63 | $ 23.63 | $ 23.63 | $ 23.63 | $ 23.63 | $ 23.63 | $ 23.63 | $ 23.63 | $ 23.63 | $ 23.63 | $ 23.63 | 283.50 | $ 23.63 | $ 23.63 |
| Total | $ 394.70 | $ 347.59 | $ 334.28 | $ 185.47 | $ 181.38 | $ 215.88 | $ 233.88 | $ 204.69 | $ 256.98 | $ 288.93 | $ 314.19 | $ 403.36 | 3,361.33 | | |

| Projected Increases | Previous Year | Projected Increase |
|---|---|---|
| Water/Sewer | $ 22.50 | 5% |
| Mobile Phone | $ 75.50 | 3% |

Current Year | Projected

# Excel Review and Assessment

## Chapter 3 Formatting Cells

### Study Quiz

*Online courseware includes a Study Quiz.*

### Features Review

*Online courseware includes a Features Review consisting of 10 multiple-choice questions to help reinforce your understanding of the chapter content.*

### Skills Review 1 **Formatting a Metric Conversion Worksheet**

**Skills**    **CH1:** Enter text, values, and dates **CH3:** Apply number formats, work with other formatting tools, adjust column width and row height, add borders, and merge cells

**Scenario**    You have created a worksheet showing common English-Metric conversions. You need to format the worksheet so it is easy to use and read.

**Steps**

1 Open the student data file named **C3R1-Metric** and save the file as **C3R1-Metric-Lastname**, but replace *Lastname* with your last name.

2 Type your name in cell A2.

3 Use the Page Layout tab to apply the Slice theme to the workbook. ***Hint:*** *Use the Themes button in the Themes group on the Page Layout tab.*

4 Apply the Title cell style to cell A1.

5 Merge and center cells A1:D1.

6 Apply the Accent6 cell style to cells A3:B3 and apply bold formatting.

7 Apply the Accent1 cell style to cells C3:D3 and apply bold formatting.

8 Decrease the number of decimal places to 0 in cells A4:A14.

9 Apply the Number format to cells C4:C14.

10 Apply a Thick Outside Border to cells A3:B14.

11 Apply a Thick Outside Border to cells C3:D14.

12 Change the row height of row 3 to *20*.

13 Merge and center cells A3:B3.

14 Merge and center cells C3:D3.

15 Change the width of columns B and D to *18*.

16 Save the workbook file.

17 Print or submit the completed file as directed by your instructor.

*Completed Review 1*

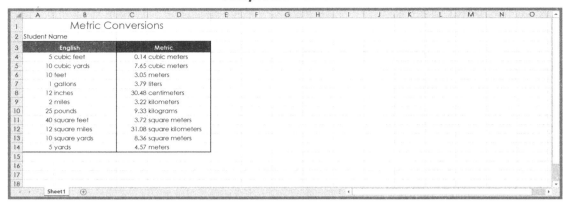

## Skills Review 2 **Formatting Stock Portfolio Information**

**Skills** **CH1:** Enter text, values, and dates; and insert and delete columns and rows
**CH3:** Apply number formats, work with other formatting tools, adjust column width and row height, apply conditional formatting, add borders, and merge cells

**Scenario** You track a portfolio of stocks and other securities using an online service such as Yahoo Finance. You are able to download daily stock quote data, but it downloads in a raw, unformatted version that makes it difficult to review. Apply formatting to make the downloaded data more attractive and useful.

**Steps**

1  Open the student data file named **C3R2-Quotes** and save the file as **C3R2-Quotes-Lastname**, but replace *Lastname* with your last name.

2  Type your name in cell A15.

3  Delete column D, which holds time information.

4  Insert two new rows at the top of the sheet and then type Quotes in cell A1.

5  Apply the Title cell style to cell A1.

6  Merge and center the contents of cells A1:G1.

7  Apply the Currency format to the cells in the *Closing Price*, *52-Week Low*, and *52-Week High* columns.

8  Apply the Percentage format with no decimal places to the cells in the *52-Week Change* column.

9  Use conditional formatting to display cells in the *52-Week Change* column that are less than 0 with Light Red Fill with Dark Red Text.

10  Apply the Comma Style format to the cells in the *Volume* column and then display the values with 0 decimal places. ***Hint:*** *Use the Comma Style button in the Number group on the Home tab.*

11  AutoFit column G.

12  Apply the Accent5 cell style to the range A3:G3, and bold and center align the text.

13  AutoFit column B.

14  Apply a Bottom Border to cells A4:G4.

15  Use the Format Painter to copy the formatting from A4:G4 to A5:G14.

16  Change the height for row 2 to 6.00, and apply the 20% - Accent2 cell style to cells A2:G2.

17  Display data bars in the *Volume* column. Apply the Orange Data Bar Gradient Fill.

18  Save the workbook file.

19  Print or submit the completed file as directed by your instructor.

### Completed Review 2

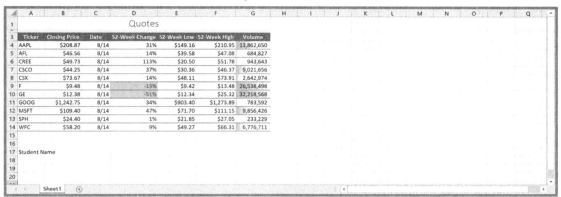

| | Ticker | Closing Price | Date | 52-Week Change | 52-Week Low | 52-Week High | Volume |
|---|---|---|---|---|---|---|---|
| 1 | | | | Quotes | | | |
| 3 | Ticker | Closing Price | Date | 52-Week Change | 52-Week Low | 52-Week High | Volume |
| 4 | AAPL | $208.87 | 8/14 | 31% | $149.16 | $210.95 | 13,862,650 |
| 5 | AFL | $46.56 | 8/14 | 14% | $39.58 | $47.08 | 684,827 |
| 6 | CREE | $49.73 | 8/14 | 113% | $20.50 | $51.78 | 943,643 |
| 7 | CSCO | $44.25 | 8/14 | 37% | $30.36 | $46.37 | 9,021,656 |
| 8 | CSX | $73.67 | 8/14 | 14% | $48.11 | $73.91 | 2,642,974 |
| 9 | F | $9.48 | 8/14 | -13% | $9.42 | $13.48 | 26,538,498 |
| 10 | GE | $12.38 | 8/14 | -51% | $12.34 | $25.32 | 32,218,568 |
| 11 | GOOG | $1,242.75 | 8/14 | 34% | $903.40 | $1,273.89 | 783,592 |
| 12 | MSFT | $109.40 | 8/14 | 47% | $71.70 | $111.15 | 9,856,426 |
| 13 | SPH | $24.40 | 8/14 | 1% | $21.85 | $27.05 | 233,229 |
| 14 | WFC | $58.20 | 8/14 | 9% | $49.27 | $66.31 | 6,776,711 |

Student Name

Sheet1

## Skills Review 3  Creating an Income Statement

**Skills**  **CH1:** Enter text, values, and dates and insert and delete columns and rows
**CH3:** Apply number formats, work with other formatting tools, adjust column width and row height, add borders, and merge cells

**Scenario**  You run a small computer company and need to prepare an income statement to track your revenues and expenses so that you can analyze how to maximize revenues and cut costs. You have entered the necessary data but need to finish the income statement worksheet by formatting it.

**Steps**

1  Open the student data file named **C3R3-Income** and save the file as **C3R3-Income-Lastname**, but replace *Lastname* with your last name.

2  Type your name in cell A20.

3  Use the Page Layout tab to apply the Ion Boardroom theme to the workbook. **Hint:** *Use the Themes button in the Themes group.*

4  Apply the Title cell style to cell A1.

5  Merge and center cells A1:D1, A2:D2, and A3:D3.

6  Select the range A2:D3, apply the 20% - Accent4 cell style, and add a Thick Outside border.

7  Apply the Accent4 cell style and Bold formatting to cells A5:D5.

8  Use Merge Across to merge cells A6:D6 and A11:D11.

9  Apply the 20% - Accent4 cell style to cells A6 and A11.

10  Apply the Accounting format with no decimal places for each year in rows 7, 10, 17, and 18.

11  Apply the Comma Style format with no decimal places for each year in rows 8, 9, and 12–16.

12  Apply a Top and Bottom border to cells A10:D10 and A17:D17.

**13** Apply the Double Underline format to cells B18:D18. *Hint: Use the Underline button arrow in the Font group on the Home tab.*

**14** Increase the height of row 1 to *30*.

**15** Delete row 4.

**16** Apply a Thick Bottom Border to cells A5:D5 and A10:D10.

**17** Save the workbook file.

**18** Print or submit the completed file as directed by your instructor.

*Completed Review 3*

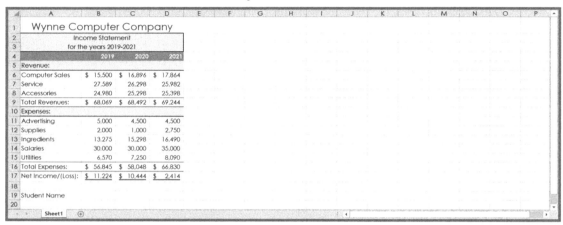

## Chapter 4 **Working with Charts**

### Study Quiz

*Online courseware includes a Study Quiz.*

### Features Review

*Online courseware includes a Features Review consisting of 10 multiple-choice questions to help reinforce your understanding of the chapter content.*

### Skills Review 1   **Charting Budget Data**

**Skills**   **CH1:** Enter text, values, and dates and explore options for printing **CH4:** Add and edit chart labels, create and move a pie chart, and modify a pie chart

**Scenario**   You have created a monthly budget to manage your finances. You have organized your spending into categories including rent, entertainment, food, car, and savings. Create a pie chart to show how much you are spending on each budget category.

**Steps**

1  Open the student data file named **C4R1-Budget** and save the file as **C4R1-Budget-Lastname**, but replace *Lastname* with your last name.

2  Type your name in cell A10.

3  Create a 3-D pie chart using the data in A3:B7.

4  Type Monthly Budget in the *Chart Title* placeholder.

5  Add data labels at the Inside End position. Display the data labels as percentages and show the category name. **Hint:** *Click the* Category Name *check box to insert a check mark.*

6  Remove the legend. **Hint:** *Click the Add Chart Element button in the Chart Layouts group on the Chart Tools Design tab, click the* Legend *option in the drop-down list, and then click the* None *option in the second drop-down list.*

7  Move the chart so that its top left corner covers cell D2.

8  Explode the *Rent* slice.

9  Change the chart style to *Style 2.* **Hint:** *Chart styles are listed in numeric order, and the style name displays as a ScreenTip when you point to a style.*

10  Change the print orientation for the entire worksheet to landscape.

11  Save the workbook file.

12  Print or submit the completed file as directed by your instructor.

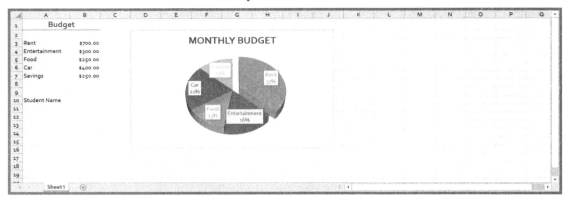

## Skills Review 2 **Comparing Temperatures**

**Skills**   **CH4:** Create a line chart and add and edit chart labels

**Scenario**   You are deciding where and when to go on your next vacation. You have charted the average monthly temperature in two cities to help you make your decision. You create a line chart to illustrate the differences in temperature.

**Steps**

1   Open the student data file named **C4R2-Temperature** and save the file as **C4R2-Temperature-Lastname**, but replace *Lastname* with your last name.

2   Insert a 2-D Line with Markers chart using the data in the range A3:C15.

3   Move the line chart to a new sheet.

4   Type Average Monthly Temperatures in the *Chart Title* placeholder.

5   Type Months as the title of the horizontal axis. ***Hint:*** *Click the Add Chart Element button in the Chart Layouts group on the Chart Tools Design tab. Click the* Axis Titles *option in the drop-down list and click the* Primary Horizontal *option in the second drop-down list. Type* Months, *and then press Enter.*

6   Type Temperature in Degrees as the title of the vertical axis. Use the hint in the previous step but click *Primary Vertical* instead of *Primary Horizontal*.

7   Use the Chart Tools Design tab to change to the Style 4 chart style. ***Hint:*** *Chart styles are listed in numeric order, and the style name displays a ScreenTip when you point to a style.*

8   Save the workbook file.

9   Print or submit the completed file as directed by your instructor.

*Completed Review 2*

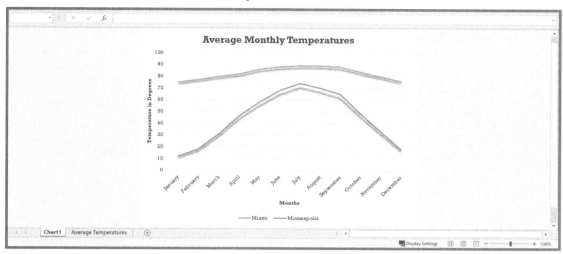

## Skills Review 3 **Charting Sales**

**Skills**   **CH4:** Create a column chart, modify chart data, and add and edit chart labels

**Scenario** You manage a sales team. You have your employees' sales numbers for the first quarter through fourth quarter of this year. You create a column chart to compare sales levels among your employees.

**Steps**

1  Open the student data file named **C4R3-Sales** and save the file as **C4R3-Sales-Lastname**, but replace *Lastname* with your last name.

2  Select the quarterly sales data for all four salespeople along with the column titles.

3  Insert a 3-D Clustered Column chart that displays the data you selected in Step 2. **Hint:** *3-D Clustered Column is the first option in the* 3-D *section of the Insert Column or Bar Chart drop-down gallery.*

4  Move the chart so the upper left corner is aligned with cell B9.

5  Type Sales Performance to replace the *Chart Title* placeholder. If requested by your instructor, save the file at this point and submit it.

6  Andre Perez has left the company. Remove his sales data from the data series, but not from the worksheet. **Hint:** *Change the chart data series to remove Andre Perez from the column chart.*

7  Click the Switch Row/Column button in the Data group on the Chart Tools Design tab. Notice how this switches the way the data is plotted. The employee names, instead of the sales quarters, now appear on the horizontal axis.

8  Apply the *Colorful Palette 2* option in the *Colorful* section of the Change Colors drop-down gallery.

9  Change the chart layout to Layout 5. **Hint:** *Click the Quick Layout button in the Chart Layouts group on the Chart Tools Design tab. Point to the fifth option in the drop-down gallery, confirm that the ScreenTip reads* Layout 5, *and then click the option.*

10  Type Sales to replace the *Axis Title* placeholder text.

11  Save the workbook file.

12  Print or submit the completed file as directed by your instructor.

*Completed Review 3*

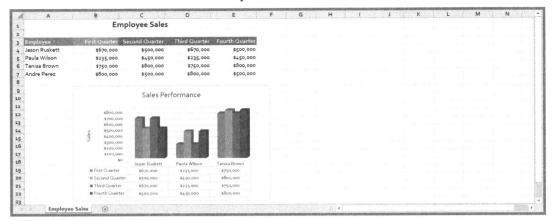

 **Skills Review 4 Charting Franchise Locations**

**Skills**     **CH4:** Create a map chart, modify chart data, and add and edit chart labels

**Scenario**  You manage a smoothie and juice company that has franchise locations throughout the United States. The company would like to expand significantly over the next few years, and you would like to share with your sales staff a visual of the number of stores located in each state so that they can start to work on their marketing and expansion strategy. You create a map chart to present the data.

**Steps**

1  Open the student data file named **C4R4-Locations** and save the file as **C4R4-Locations-Lastname**, but replace *Lastname* with your last name.

2  Select the range A1:B16.

3  Insert a map chart that displays the data you selected in Step 2. If a warning box displays, click the Accept button.

4  Move the chart so the upper left corner is aligned with cell D2.

5  Type Store Locations by State to replace the *Chart Title* placeholder.

6  Use the Chart Elements button to add data labels to the chart.

7  Apply the *Colorful Palette 4* option. **Hint:** *Use the Chart Styles button and select the Color tab.*

8  Save the workbook file.

9  Print or submit the completed file as directed by your instructor.

*Completed Review 4*

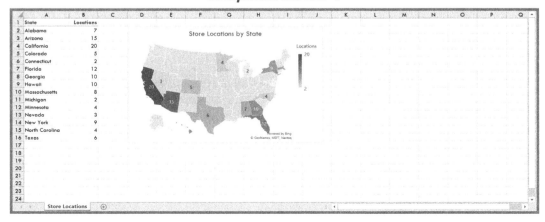

# Excel Review and Assessment

## Unit 5 Microsoft Excel

### Skills Assessment 1 Population Statistics

**Skills** **CH1:** Understand worksheet and workbook structure; use cell references; enter text, values, and dates; add, rename, move, and delete worksheets; and explore options for printing **CH2:** Enter a function, edit cell contents, sort data, and use Show Formulas **CH3:** Work with other formatting tools, adjust column width and row height, and merge cells **CH4:** Create a map chart, and add and edit chart labels

**Scenario** You are working in a marketing department. Your company is going to test-market a new product to see if it sells. The marketing campaign will initially target one of the six largest cities in the United States. You have been asked to prepare a spreadsheet and chart that show the population in these cities.

**Steps**

1 Create a new, blank workbook file in Excel and name it **U5A1-Population-Lastname**, but replace *Lastname* with your last name.

2 Type Population Statistics in cell A1.

3 Merge and center cells A1:C1.

4 Format cell A1 with the Heading 1 cell style.

5 Change the theme to Vapor Trail. ***Hint:*** *You may need to scroll down to locate this option in the Themes drop-down gallery.*

6 Type the following data in cells A3:C9:

| City | State | Population |
|------|-------|-----------|
| Chicago | Illinois | 2,716,450 |
| Houston | Texas | 2,312,717 |
| Los Angeles | California | 3,999,759 |
| New York | New York | 8,550,698 |
| Philadelphia | Pennsylvania | 1,580,863 |
| Phoenix | Arizona | 1,626,078 |

7 In cell B11, type Total.

8 In cell B12, type Minimum.

9 In cell B13, type Maximum.

10 Right-align and bold the labels in B11:B13.

11 Use the appropriate function to insert the total population for the listed cities in cell C11.

12 Use the appropriate function to insert the lowest population in cell C12.

13 Edit the population for New York, New York to read *8,622,698*.

14 Use the appropriate function to insert the highest population in cell C13.

15 AutoFit columns A, B, and C.

16 Select cells A3:C3 and then format the cells with the Accent5 cell style.

17 Sort the data by Population in descending order.

18 Select cells A3:C9 and then insert a map chart.

19 Change the chart style to Style 3.

**20** Move the chart so that the top left corner of the chart is in cell E2.

**21** Change the chart title to Largest U.S. Cities.

**22** Change the name of Sheet 1, typing Population as the new name.

**23** Change the print orientation for the worksheet to landscape.

**24** Save the workbook file.

**25** Print a copy of the worksheet or submit the completed file as directed by your instructor.

**26** Show formulas in the worksheet.

**27** Print a copy of the worksheet or submit the completed file as directed by your instructor.
*Note: You have now printed a copy showing data and then another copy showing formulas.*

### *Completed Assessment 1, Step 25*

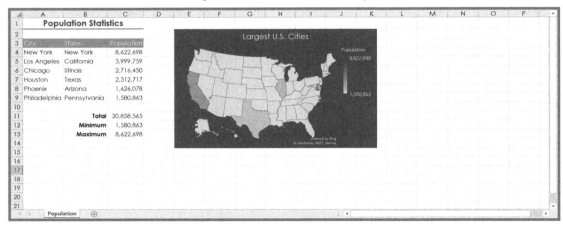

## Skills Assessment 2 **Calories Burned During Exercise Worksheet**

**Skills** **CH1:** Understand worksheet and workbook structure; enter text, values, and dates; use the spelling checker; insert headers and footers; and explore options for printing **CH2:** Filter data and insert a function **CH3:** Apply number formats, work with other formatting tools, adjust column width and row height, apply conditional formatting, and merge cells **CH4:** Create a column chart and add and edit chart labels

**Scenario** You are researching an article for *Guidelines for Healthy Living Magazine*. You want to show readers how they can burn calories while on vacation without having to go to the gym. You create a worksheet with a column chart that shows examples of calories burned, noting that calories burned are affected by body weight.

**Steps**

**1** Open the student data file named **U5A2-Exercise** and save the file as **U5A2-Exercise-Lastname**, but replace *Lastname* with your last name.

**2** Merge and center cells A1:D1.

**3** Format cell A1 with the Heading 1 cell style.

**4** Merge and center cells B2:D2.

**5** Apply the Accent2 cell style and bold formatting to cell B2.

6  Apply the Accent6 cell style to cell A3.

7  Apply the Accent1 cell style to cells B3:D3.

8  Make cell A1 active and then spell check the worksheet, ignoring all suggestions to change the abbreviation *lbs* and accepting the suggested changes to correct the two spelling errors.

9  Insert a function to enter today's date in cell A11 and apply the Long Date format. AutoFit column A so that the date displays in its entirety.

10  Right-align cells B3:D3.

11  Change the width of columns B, C, and D to 10.00.

12  Change the height of row 1 to 24.00.

13  Use conditional formatting to display data bars in cells B4:D8 with the *Gradient Fill Orange Data Bar* option.

14  Select the range A3:D8 and then insert a 2-D Clustered Column chart.

15  Type Calories Burned to replace the *Chart Title* placeholder.

16  Move the chart so that the top left corner of the chart is in cell F2.

17  Change the chart style to *Style 9*.

18  Add a title to the vertical axis (Primary Vertical axis), typing Calories as the new title.

19  Add a title to the horizontal axis (Primary Horizontal axis), typing Exercise as the new title.

20  Filter the worksheet data to remove the Windsurfing data. Notice the chart automatically updates to only display the filtered data.

21  Type your name in cell A10.

22  Insert the file name in the header and then return to Normal view.

23  Change the page orientation to landscape for the worksheet.

24  Save the workbook file.

25  Print a copy of the worksheet using the *Fit Sheet on One Page* print option or submit the completed file as directed by your instructor.

### Completed Assessment 2

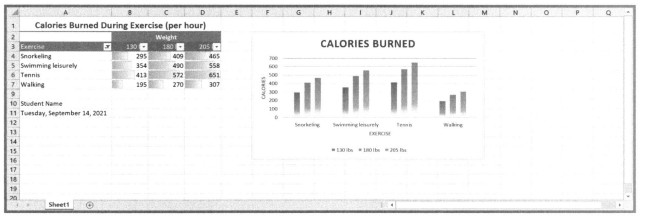

## Skills Assessment 3  Employee Salary Calculations Worksheet

**Skills**   **CH1:** Understand worksheet and workbook structure; use cell references; enter text, values, and dates; add, rename, move, and delete worksheets and explore options for printing **CH2:** Enter a formula, enter a function, insert a function, use AutoSum, use absolute and relative cell references, and copy and move cell contents **CH3:** Apply number formats, work with other formatting tools, adjust column width and row height, add borders, and merge cells **CH4:** Add and edit chart labels, create a pie chart, and modify a pie chart

**Scenario**   You are in charge of calculating the payroll for the employees at Paradigm Steel. The employees receive a base salary plus commission. You need to calculate new salary figures for all the employees because all employees will receive a 5.25 percent raise. You use a pie chart to display the results in an easy-to-read format.

**Steps**

1  Open the student data file named **U5A3-Steel** and save the file as **U5A3-Steel-Lastname**, but replace *Lastname* with your last name.

2  Change the width of column A to 22.00. Change the width of column B to 13.00. Change the width of columns C through G to 16.00.

3  Type the title Commission in cell E2.

4  In cell E3, calculate the commission using a formula that multiplies projected sales by the commission rate. ***Hint:*** *Use an absolute reference for cell B18.* Copy the formula in cell E3 to cells E4:E12.

5  Type the title Salary in cell F2.

6  In cell F3, calculate the salary by adding the base salary and the commission. Copy the formula in cell F3 to cells F4:F12.

7  Type the title New Salary in cell G2.

8  Employees will all receive a 5.25 percent raise on their base salary. In cell G3, calculate the new salary using the formula Base Salary + (Base Salary * Raise) + Commission. ***Hint:*** *Use an absolute cell reference in your formula.* Copy the formula in cell G3 to cells G4:G12.

9  Apply the Currency format with no decimal places to the values in columns C through G.

10  Set the height of rows 13 through 16 to 22.50.

11  Right align the *Total*, *Average*, *Lowest*, and *Highest* labels and apply bold formatting. Move these labels from cells A13:A16 to cells B13:B16.

12  Use the appropriate functions to calculate the *Total*, *Average*, *Lowest*, and *Highest* values for columns C through G.

13  Merge and center cells A1:G1 and set the row height of row 1 to 48.00.

14  Apply the Title cell style to cell A1.

15  Set the row height of row 2 to 20.25.

16  Apply the Integral theme.

17  Center the column headers in row 2, apply the Accent5 cell style, and apply bold formatting.

18  Add a thick outside border around the column headers in row 2.

19  Apply the Accent2 cell style to cells C13 though G13, Accent3 cell style to cells C14 through G14, Accent4 cell style to cells C15 through G15, and Accent5 cell style to cells C16 through G16.

20  Type your name in cell A20.

21 Change the page orientation to landscape.

22 Create a 3-D pie chart of the new salaries for all employees. *Hint: Use the Ctrl key to highlight A2:A12 and G2:G12 before creating the chart.*

23 Move the location of the chart to a new worksheet and rename the sheet, typing Salary Chart as the new name.

24 Use the Chart Elements button to add data labels that display the category name at the Inside End position along with the already displayed salary value.

25 Change the chart style to Style 8.

26 Modify the chart title, typing EMPLOYEE 2021 SALARIES as the new chart title.

27 Rename Sheet1, typing Data as the new worksheet name.

28 Save the workbook file.

29 Print copies of the worksheet and the chart sheet or submit the completed file as directed by your instructor.

### Completed Assessment 3 Data

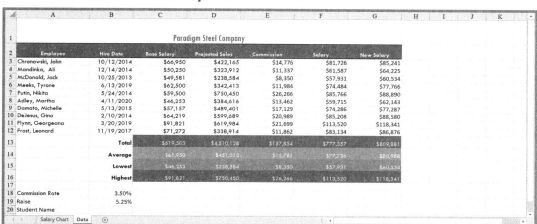

### Completed Assessment 3 Salary Chart

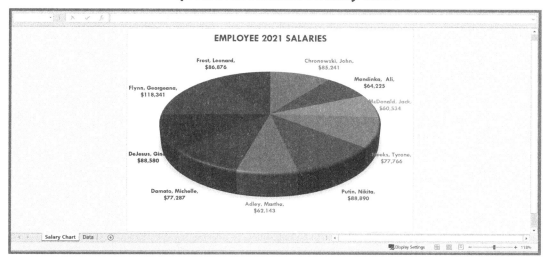

# UNIT 6

# Access Review and Assessment

Chapter 1    **Working with Databases**

Chapter 2    **Creating Forms and Tables**

Chapter 3    **Working with Queries
and Reports**

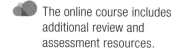 The online course includes additional review and assessment resources.

# Access Review and Assessment

## Chapter 1 **Working with Databases**

### Study Quiz

*Online courseware includes a Study Quiz.*

### Features Review

*Online courseware includes a Features Review consisting of 10 multiple-choice questions to help reinforce your understanding of the chapter content.*

### Skills Review 1 **Updating and Sorting an Organic Food Store Database**

**Skills**  **CH1:** Open and navigate a database, enter data, edit data, and sort data

**Scenario**  You are in charge of updating the records in a database for an organic food store. You add some new items to the database and edit an existing record. You also sort a datasheet to make it easier to find information in the table.

**Steps**

1  Open the student data file named **C1R1-OrganicProducts**. If a security warning appears immediately below the ribbon, click the Enable Content button. If a second security warning appears, click the Yes button.

2  Open the Customers table.

3  In record 3, edit the contents of the *LastName* field to read *Katz* instead of *Kati*.

4  AutoFit the Address column.

5  Close the Customers table.

6  Open the Products form.

7  On the Record Navigation bar, click the New (blank) record button.

8  Add the following information to create three new records:

| ProductNo | ProductName | AllergenInfo |
|-----------|-------------|--------------|
| 5172 | Ancient Grains Cereal | wheat |
| 8322 | Organic Cottage Cheese | milk |
| 8347 | Organic Cream Cheese | milk |

9  Close the Products form.

10  Open the Inventory table.

11  Add the following information to create three new records:

| ProductNo | Quantity |
|-----------|----------|
| 5172 | 87 |
| 8322 | 98 |
| 8347 | 103 |

12  Sort the Inventory table by the *Quantity* field in ascending order.

13  Save the Inventory table without closing it. **Hint:** *Click the Save button on the Quick Access Toolbar.*

14  Print the Inventory table or submit the completed database as directed by your instructor.

15  Remove the sort and save the Inventory table again.

16  Close the Inventory table and then the database.

## Completed Review 1, Step 4

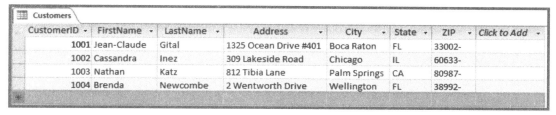

## Completed Review 1, Step 8

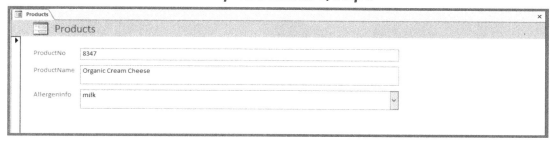

## Completed Review 1, Step 12

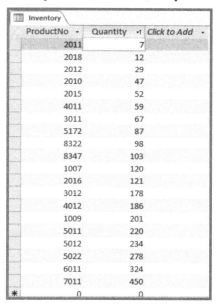

## Skills Review 2 Filtering a Database of Exercises

**Skills**    **CH1:** Open and navigate a database, filter data, and use existing queries and reports

**Scenario**  You are a personal trainer. You have created a database of exercises so that you can easily develop exercise plans for your clients. You are working with a new client, and you filter the records and run existing queries to provide your client with exercise options.

**Steps**

1   Open the student data file named **C1R2-Exercises**. If a security warning appears immediately below the ribbon, click the Enable Content button. If a second security warning appears, click the Yes button.

2   Open the NoEquipmentRequired query to display all the exercises that do not require exercise equipment.

3   Close the NoEquipmentRequired query.

4   Open the StrengthExercises query to display all of the exercises designed for strength training.

5   Close the StrengthExercises query.

6   Your client is interested in working on abs. To show the client appropriate exercise options, open the Exercises table.

7   Filter the *MuscleGroup* column so that only the Abs records are displayed.

8   Print the Exercises table or submit the completed database as directed by your instructor.

9   Toggle the filter to turn it off and save the Exercises table again. **Hint:** *Click the Save button on the Quick Access Toolbar.*

10  Close the Exercises table and then the database.

### Completed Review 2, Step 2

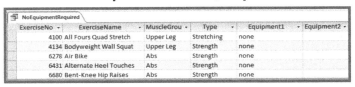

### Completed Review 2, Step 4

### Completed Review 2, Step 7

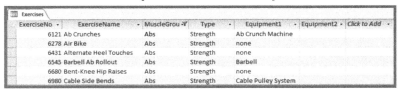

## Skills Review 3 **Tracking Community Volunteers**

**Skills**  **CH1:** Open and navigate a database, sort data, format a datasheet, and use existing queries and reports

**Scenario**  You work in the student records office at your school and have set up a database to track student community service hours. This data is important because many students volunteer to meet graduation or financial aid requirements. To make the data easy for others in your office to use, you sort the database, format a datasheet, and display a report.

**Steps**

1 Open the student data file named **C1R3-CommunityService**. If a security warning appears immediately below the ribbon, click the Enable Content button. If a second security warning appears, click the Yes button.

2 Open the Organizations report to display information about the community agencies at which students can volunteer.

3 Close the Organizations report.

4 Open the VolunteerHours table.

5 Change the font size to 12 points.

6 Center the entries in the fields in the *ServiceDate* column.

7 Sort the table by the *OrganizationName* column in ascending order.

8 Save the changes to the VolunteerHours table without closing it. **Hint:** *Click the Save button on the Quick Access Toolbar.*

9 Print the VolunteerHours table or submit the completed file as directed by your instructor.

10 Close the VolunteerHours table and then the database.

### Completed Review 3, Step 2

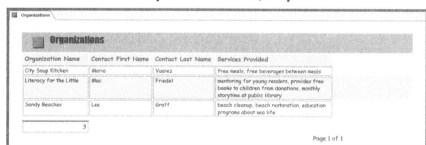

### Completed Review 3, Step 7

# Access Review and Assessment

## Chapter 2 **Creating Forms and Tables**

### Study Quiz

*Online courseware includes a Study Quiz.*

### Features Review

*Online courseware includes a Features Review consisting of 10 multiple-choice questions to help reinforce your understanding of the chapter content.*

### Skills Review 1  **Adding to the Database for an Organic Food Store**

**Skills**  **CH1:** Open and navigate a database, enter data, and format a datasheet
**CH2:** Create a table, enter data in a table, create a form, and enter data in a form

**Scenario**  You are in charge of updating a database for an organic food store. You need to add a new table to the existing database. The table will store information about upcoming product promotions. You also need to add data to the new table.

**Steps**

1  Open the student data file named **C2R1-OrganicProducts**. If a security warning appears immediately below the ribbon, click the Enable Content button. If a second security warning appears, click the Yes button.

2  Create a new table in Design view.

3  Add the following three fields to the table:

| Field Name | Data Type |
| --- | --- |
| ProductNo | Number |
| Event | Short Text |
| Discount | Currency |

4  Make the *ProductNo* field the primary key.

5  Save the table, typing Events as the table name.

6  Close the Events table.

7  Create a form based on the Events table.

8  Save the form, accepting the form name *Events*.

9  Open the Events form in Form view and then add three new records containing the following information. ***Hint:*** *Press the Tab key after each entry.*

| ProductNo | Event | Discount |
| --- | --- | --- |
| 2018 | Summer Cool-off | 1.00 |
| 3011 | Product Launch | 0.75 |
| 3012 | Product Launch | 0.50 |

10  Close the Events form.

11  Open the Events table.

12  Copy the first record, which has the product number 2018.

13  Paste the copied record as the fourth record.

14  Change the *ProductNo* entry for the fourth record, typing 2015 as the new entry.

15  Adjust the width of the *Event* column in the datasheet so that all the data is visible.

16  Save the database.

17  Print the Events table or submit the completed database as directed by your instructor.

18  Close the Events table and then the database.

*Completed Review 1, Events Form*

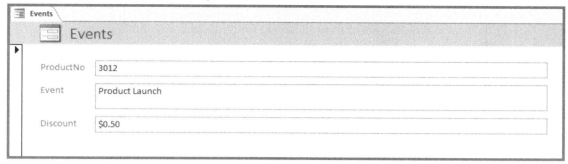

*Completed Review 1, Events Table*

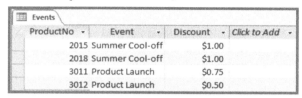

## Skills Review 2 Expanding an Exercises Database

**Skills** **CH1:** Open and navigate a database **CH2:** Create a table, enter data in a table, create a form, and enter data in a form

**Scenario** You are a personal trainer. You need to expand your existing database to include a table with client contact information. To make entering client data easier, you specify values for the *Schedule* field and create a form.

**Steps**

1 Open the student data file named **C2R2-Exercises**. If a security warning appears immediately below the ribbon, click the Enable Content button. If a second security warning appears, click the Yes button.

2 Create a new table in Design view.

3 Add the following five fields to the table:

| Field Name | Data Type |
| --- | --- |
| ClientID | AutoNumber |
| LastName | Short Text |
| FirstName | Short Text |
| Email | Short Text |
| Schedule | Lookup Wizard |

4 In the Lookup Wizard dialog box, specify your own values in a single column, typing the following entries:
Orientation
Daily
Two times a week
Three times a week

When you are done, click the Finish button to apply your entries and close the dialog box.

5 Make the *ClientID* field the primary key.

6 Save the table, typing Clients as the table name.

7 Close the table.

8  Create a form based on the Clients table.

9  Switch to Design view, and then narrow the width of the fields in the form by dragging the right border of the *ClientID* field to the 5-inch mark on the ruler.

10  Save the form, typing Clients as the form name.

11  Switch to Form view.

12  Add three new records containing the following information. **Note:** *Press Tab in the* ClientID *field to enter an AutoNumber.*

| LastName | FirstName | Email | Schedule |
|----------|-----------|-------|----------|
| Wilson | Joe | jwilson@ppi-edu.net | Orientation |
| Ryan | Mariah | mryan@ppi-edu.net | Daily |
| Perez | Andrea | aperez@ppi-edu.net | Daily |

13  Close the form.

14  Open the Clients table and AutoFit the *Email* field.

15  Save the table.

16  Print the Clients table or submit the completed database as directed by your instructor.

17  Close the Clients table and then the database.

### Completed Review 2, Clients Form

### Completed Review 2, Clients Table

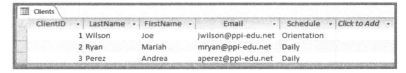

## Skills Review 3 **Tracking Community Service Hours**

**Skills**  **CH1:** Open and navigate a database **CH2:** Create a form and create a relationship between tables

**Scenario**  You have created a database to track hours that students spend doing community service. In this exercise, you create forms to make it easier to enter data in two of the tables in the database.

**Steps**

1  Open the student data file named **C2R3-CommunityService**. If a security warning appears immediately below the ribbon, click the Enable Content button. If a second security warning appears, click the Yes button.

2  Create a form based on the VolunteerHours table.

3  Switch to Design view, and then narrow the width of the fields in the form by dragging the right border of the *DonationID* field to the 5-inch mark on the ruler.

4  Save the form, naming it *VolunteerHours*.

5  Switch to Layout view.

6  Add the date and time to the form header, accepting the default settings in the Date and Time dialog box.

7  Save and then close the updated form.

8  Create a form based on the Organizations table.

9  Save the form, naming it *Organizations* and then close the form.

10  Create a form based on the Students table.

11  Save the form, naming it *Students* and then close the form.

12  Open the Relationships window. If necessary, add the Organizations, VolunteerHours, and Students table to the window. Next, create a one-to-many relationship between the *OrganizationName* fields in the Organizations and Volunteer Hours tables. Click the *Enforce Referential Integrity* option.

13  Create a one-to-many relationship between the *StudentID* fields in the Students and VolunteerHours tables. Click the *Enforce Referential Integrity* option.

14  Save and then close the Relationships window.

15  Print the VolunteerHours, Organizations, and Students forms or submit the database as directed by your instructor.

16  Close the database.

## Completed Review 3, VolunteerHours Form

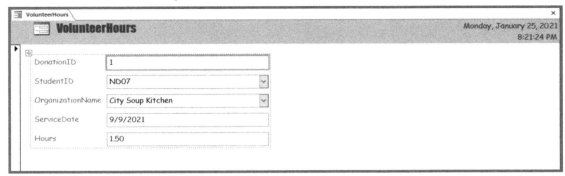

## Completed Review 3, Organizations Form

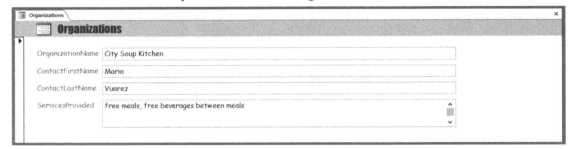

## Completed Review 3, Students Form

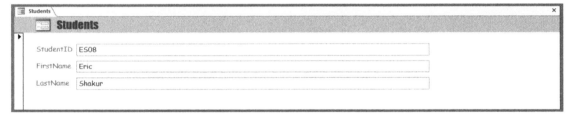

## Completed Review 3, Relationships Window

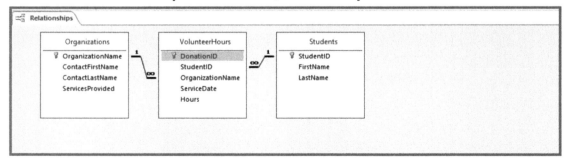

# Access Review and Assessment

## Chapter 3 Working with Queries and Reports

### Study Quiz

*Online courseware includes a Study Quiz.*

### Features Review

*Online courseware includes a Features Review consisting of 10 multiple-choice questions to help reinforce your understanding of the chapter content.*

### Skills Review 1 Checking Inventory by Querying an Organic Products Database

**Skills**    **CH1:** Open and navigate a database and format a datasheet **CH3:** Create a query in Design view, use more than one table in a query, and create and preview a report

**Scenario**   You are the purchaser for a large grocery store, and you need to find out which organic products to reorder this week. You query the organic products database to find this information.

**Steps**

1. Open the student data file named **C3R1-OrganicProducts**. If a security warning appears immediately below the ribbon, click the Enable Content button. If a second security warning appears, click the Yes button.

2. Use Design view to create a query using data from the Products table and the Inventory table. The *ProductNo* fields in the Products and Inventory tables have a one-to-one relationship.

3. Define the query to find all products with fewer than 100 items in stock and to display the *ProductNo*, *ProductName*, and *Quantity* fields, in that order.

4. Save the query, typing InventoryUnder100 as the query name. Run the query to confirm that it is selecting the correct records.

5. Close the InventoryUnder100 query.

6. In the Navigation pane, click *InventoryUnder100* in the Queries group.

7. Using the Report button, create a report based on the InventoryUnder100 query.

8. Apply the Integral theme to the report.

9. AutoFit the *Record Count* cell. **Hint:** *The name of the cell appears in a ScreenTip.*

10. Edit the *Report Header* to read *Inventory Under 100*. **Hint:** *Click the Report Header, open the Property Sheet, and then edit the Caption property.*

11. Edit the *ProductNo* column heading to read *Product No*.

12. Edit the *ProductName* column heading to read *Product Name* and then close the Property Sheet.

13. Save the report, naming it *InventoryUnder100*.

14. Print the InventoryUnder100 report or submit the completed database as directed by your instructor.

15. Close the InventoryUnder100 report and then the database.

### Completed Review 1, InventoryUnder100 Query

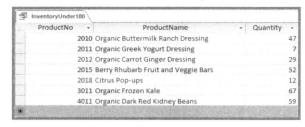

### Completed Review 1, InventoryUnder100 Report

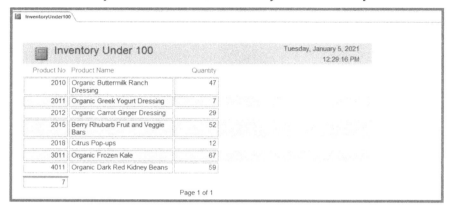

 ## Skills Review 2  Finding Information in an Exercises Database

**Skills**  **CH1:** Open and navigate a database **CH3:** Use the Query Wizard and use the Report Wizard

**Scenario**  You are a personal trainer and are preparing to send an email reminding your clients of the many exercises they can do without any equipment. You will query the Exercises database to find the contact information for your clients. You also create a report named NoEquipmentRequired based on an existing query in the database.

**Steps**

1  Open the student data file named **C3R2-Exercises**. If a security warning appears immediately below the ribbon, click the Enable Content button. If a second security warning appears, click the Yes button.

2  In the Navigation pane, click *Clients* in the Tables group.

3  Use the Query Wizard to create a simple query that lists the *LastName, FirstName,* and *Email* fields, in that order.

4  Save the query, naming it *ClientsQuery*.

5  Save and then close the ClientsQuery query.

6  In the Navigation pane, click *NoEquipmentRequired* in the Queries group.

7  Use the Report Wizard to create a report based on the NoEquipmentRequired query. The report should display the *ExerciseName, MuscleGroup,* and *Type* fields, in that order. Do not specify any grouping levels. Sort the report by the *ExerciseName* field in ascending order.

8  Edit the *Report Header* to read *No Equipment Required.* **Hint:** *Click the Report Header, open the Property Sheet, and then edit the Caption property.* If necessary, widen the *Report Header* to display the text in its entirety.

9    Edit the *ExerciseName* column heading to read *Exercise Name*.

10   Edit the *MuscleGroup* column heading to read *Muscle Group,* and then close the Property Sheet.

11   Save the report, naming it *NoEquipmentRequired*.

12   Use the Print Preview feature to preview the report.

13   Print the NoEquipmentRequired report or submit the completed database as directed by your instructor.

14   Close the NoEquipmentRequired report and then the database.

### Completed Review 2, ClientsQuery

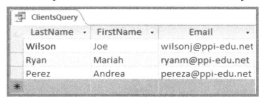

### Completed Review 2, NoEquipmentRequired Report

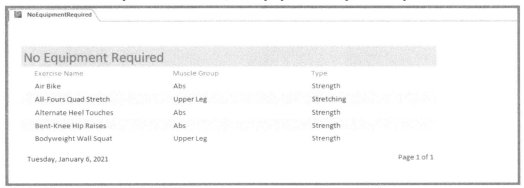

## Skills Review 3   Finding and Reporting Information from a Community Volunteers Database

**Skills**     **CH1:** Open and navigate a database, and format a datasheet **CH3:** Create a query in Design view, use more than one table in a query, and create and preview a report

**Scenario**  You have set up a database to track the number of hours students spend performing community service. You first find out how many hours students are volunteering at the various organizations and then present that information in a report.

**Steps**

1    Open the student data file named **C3R3-CommunityService**. If a security warning appears immediately below the ribbon, click the Enable Content button. If a second security warning appears, click the Yes button.

2    Query the database to find out how many volunteer hours are being spent at each organization. In Design view, add the Organizations table and then the VolunteerHours table to create your query. The query should display the *OrganizationName* field (from the Organizations table), *StudentID* field (from the VolunteerHours table), and *Hours* field (from the VolunteerHours table), in that order. Sort the query by *OrganizationName* in ascending order.

3 Run the query to confirm that it is selecting the correct records.

4 Save the query, typing VolunteerHoursByOrganization as the query name, and then close the query.

5 Use the Report button to create a report based on the VolunteerHoursByOrganization query.

6 Display the Group, Sort, and Total pane and then group the report by the *OrganizationName* field.

7 Sort the report by the *Hours* field.

8 Close the Group, Sort, and Total pane.

9 AutoFit the *Record Count* cell.

10 Edit the *Report Header* to read *Volunteer Hours by Organization*. **Hint:** *Click the Report Header, open the Property Sheet, and then edit the Caption property.*

11 Edit the *OrganizationName* column heading to read *Organization Name*.

12 Edit the *StudentID* column heading to read *Student ID* and then close the Property Sheet.

13 Save the report, naming it *VolunteerHoursByOrganization*.

14 View the report using Print Preview.

15 Change the print orientation to landscape.

16 Print the VolunteerHoursByOrganization report or submit the completed document as directed by your instructor.

17 Save and close the VolunteerHoursByOrganization report and then close the database.

### *Completed Review 3, VolunteerHoursByOrganization Query*

| OrganizationName | StudentID | Hours |
|---|---|---|
| City Soup Kitchen | LP06 | 2.25 |
| City Soup Kitchen | RS08 | 1.5 |
| City Soup Kitchen | ES08 | 2.5 |
| City Soup Kitchen | SS06 | 2 |
| City Soup Kitchen | ND07 | 1.5 |
| Literacy for the Little | VS07 | 3 |
| Literacy for the Little | LP06 | 3.5 |
| Literacy for the Little | MJ07 | 2 |
| Literacy for the Little | TI08 | 2.25 |
| Sandy Beaches | ES08 | 2.25 |
| Sandy Beaches | VS07 | 3 |
| Sandy Beaches | SK06 | 3 |

# Completed Review 3, VolunteerHoursByOrganization Report

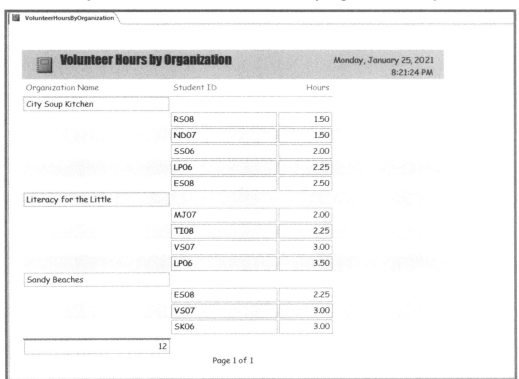

VolunteerHoursByOrganization

## Volunteer Hours by Organization
Monday, January 25, 2021
8:21:24 PM

| Organization Name | Student ID | Hours |
|---|---|---|
| City Soup Kitchen | | |
| | RS08 | 1.50 |
| | ND07 | 1.50 |
| | SS06 | 2.00 |
| | LP06 | 2.25 |
| | ES08 | 2.50 |
| Literacy for the Little | | |
| | MJ07 | 2.00 |
| | TI08 | 2.25 |
| | VS07 | 3.00 |
| | LP06 | 3.50 |
| Sandy Beaches | | |
| | ES08 | 2.25 |
| | VS07 | 3.00 |
| | SK06 | 3.00 |
| 12 | | |

Page 1 of 1

## Unit **6 Microsoft Access**

### Skills Assessment 1  **A Movie Database**

**Skills**   **CH1:** Open and navigate a database, enter data, edit data, and format a datasheet
**CH2:** Create a table, create a relationship between tables, create a form, and enter data in a form **CH3:** Create a query in Design view and create and preview a report

**Scenario**   You manage a business that streams movies online. You have created a database to store data on the available movies. You now need to create a table to store information about each movie and then create a form and use it to enter records in the database. Finally, you need to run a query to find all the PG-13 movies in your database, and you create a report based on that query.

**Steps**

1   Open the student data file named **U6A1-Movies**.

2   Create a new table in Design view.

3   Define the table to have the following fields and data types:

| Field Name | Data Type |
|------------|-----------|
| MovieID | Number |
| Title | Short Text |
| Rating | Lookup Wizard |

4   In the Lookup Wizard dialog box, specify your own values in a single column, typing the following entries:
PG
PG-13
R

Close the dialog box when you are done.

5   Make the *MovieID* field the primary key.

6   Save the table, typing *Movies* as the table name, and then close the table.

7   Use the Form button to create a form based on the Movies table.

8   Switch to Design view and then narrow the width of the fields in the form by dragging the right border of the *MovieID* field to the 5-inch mark on the ruler.

9   Save the form, naming it *Movies*.

10   Switch to Form view.

11   Use the Movies form to enter the following records in the database:

| ID | Title | Rating |
|------|-------------------------|--------|
| 3185 | Mamma Mia! | PG-13 |
| 3479 | Christopher Robin | PG |
| 3480 | Ocean's 8 | PG-13 |
| 3529 | Avengers: Infinity War | PG-13 |
| 4690 | A Quiet Place | PG-13 |
| 5134 | A Wrinkle in Time | PG |

12   Change the *MovieID* number of the first record to 3155.

13   In Design view, create a query to find all movies rated PG-13. Display the fields *Title* and then *Rating* in your query.

**14** Run the query and AutoFit the *Title* column.

**15** Save the query, typing PG-13Movies as the query name.

**16** Print the PG-13Movies query or submit the query result as directed by your instructor. Close the query.

**17** Use the Report button to create a report based on the PG-13Movies query.

**18** Sort the report in descending order by the *Title* field.

**19** AutoFit the *Record Count* cell.

**20** Open the Property Sheet and change the *Caption* property to *PG-13 Movies*.

**21** Save the report, naming it *PG-13Movies*, and then close the report.

**22** Run the PG-13Movies report. Print the report or submit the report result as directed by your instructor. Close the report.

**23** Create a new table in Design view.

**24** Define the table to have the following fields and data types:

| Field Name | Data Type |
| --- | --- |
| ID | AutoNumber |
| Actor | Short Text |
| MovieID | Number |

**25** Make the *ID* field the primary key.

**26** Save the table, typing *Actors* as the table name, and then close the table.

**27** Open the Relationships window. If necessary, click the Show Table button and then add the Actors and Movies tables to the Relationships window.

**28** Create a relationship between the Actors and Movies tables by creating a one-to-many relationship between the *MovieID* fields. Click the *Enforce Referential Integrity* option. Close the Relationships window.

**29** Open the Actors table in Datasheet view and enter the following records:

| ID | Actor | MovieID |
| --- | --- | --- |
| 1 | Meryl Streep | 3155 |
| 2 | Pierce Brosnan | 3155 |
| 3 | Sandra Bullock | 3480 |
| 4 | Cate Blanchett | 3529 |
| 5 | Emily Blunt | 4690 |
| 6 | Mindy Kaling | 4690 |
| 7 | Mindy Kaling | 5134 |

**30** Save and then close the table.

**31** Use the Query Wizard to create a query that displays the *Actor* field from the Actors table and the *Title* field from the Movies table. **Hint:** *Use the* Tables/Queries *option box arrow to change the table name when selecting fields. Change the query title to* ActorMovies.

**32** Close the query.

**33** Close the database and submit the completed file as directed by your instructor.

### Completed Assessment 1, Movies Form

### Completed Assessment 1, PG-13Movies Query

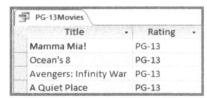

### Completed Assessment 1, PG-13Movies Report

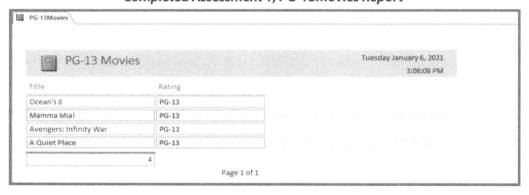

### Completed Assessment 1, Actors Table

### Completed Assessment 1, ActorMovies Query

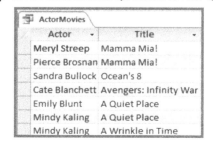

# Skills Assessment 2  A Computer Support Service Database

**Skills**     **CH1:** Open and navigate a database and enter data **CH2:** Create a table, create a form, and enter data in a form **CH3:** Create a query in Design view and use the Report Wizard

**Scenario**   You run a computer support website. Users pay either a six-month fee of $60 or an annual fee of $120 to access online computer help. You need to create a database to store information about your subscribers. After creating a table and entering customer records, you then run a query to find the customers who have paid $60 for six months of service, and you create a report based on that query.

**Steps**

1   Open the student data file named **U6A2-ComputerSupport**.

2   Create a new table in Design view.

3   Define the table to have the following fields and data types:

| Field Name | Data Type |
| --- | --- |
| ID | Number |
| LastName | Short Text |
| FirstName | Short Text |
| JoinMonth | Lookup Wizard |
| Fee | Currency |

4   In the Lookup Wizard dialog box, specify your own values in a single column, typing the following entries:
January
February
March
April
May
June
July
August
September
October
November
December

5   Make the *ID* field the primary key.

6   Save the table, typing Customers as the table name. Close the table.

7   Use the Form button to create a form based on the Customers table.

8   Switch to Design view, and then narrow the width of the fields in the form by dragging the right border of the *ID* field to the 5-inch mark on the ruler.

9   Save the form, naming it *Customers*.

10   Switch to Form view.

11   Use the Customers form in Form view to enter the following records in the database:

| ID | LastName | FirstName | JoinMonth | Fee |
| --- | --- | --- | --- | --- |
| 5155 | Mitchell | Paul | September | 120.00 |
| 5167 | Ableson | Michelle | October | 60.00 |
| 5169 | Quinn | Terry | October | 60.00 |
| 5170 | Samuels | Jennifer | November | 60.00 |
| 5180 | Watson | Robert | November | 120.00 |
| 5290 | Simpson | Ann | December | 120.00 |
| 5400 | Gregory | Michaela | December | 60.00 |

**12** Close the Customers form.

**13** Use the Query Design button to create a query of all customers who have paid a fee of $60. Display the *LastName*, *FirstName*, and *Fee* fields, in that order, in the query.

**14** Run the query.

**15** Save the query, typing $60Customers as the query name.

**16** Print the $60Customers query or submit the query result as directed by your instructor. Close the query.

**17** Use the Report Wizard button to create a report based on the $60Customers query. Include the *LastName*, *FirstName*, and *Fee* fields in the report. Do not add any grouping levels.

**18** Sort the report in ascending order based on the *LastName* field and accept the default report layout.

**19** Edit the *Report Header* to read *$60 Customers*. **Hint:** *Open the Property Sheet and edit the Caption property.*

**20** Save the report, naming it *$60Customers*, and then close the report.

**21** Run the $60Customers report. Print the report or submit the report result as directed by your instructor. Close the report.

**22** Close the database and submit the completed file as directed by your instructor.

*Completed Assessment 2, Customers Form*

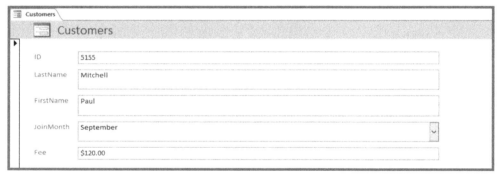

*Completed Assessment 2, $60Customers Query*

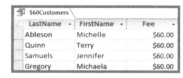

*Completed Assessment 2, $60Customers Report*

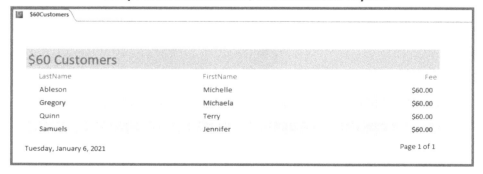

## Skills Assessment 3  A Rental Car Database

**Skills**   **CH1:** Open and navigate a database, enter data, sort data, and filter data **CH2:** Create a table, enter data in a table, create a relationship between tables, create a form, and enter data in a form **CH3:** Create a query in Design view, and create and preview a report

**Scenario**   You run a car rental company and are setting up a database to track your car inventory and reservations. You add to the existing database by creating a table and adding records to the table. You then create a form for adding additional records to the table, and you filter the data in the table. Finally, you create a relationship between tables, run a query to find all the reservations on file, and create a report based on that query.

**Steps**

1  Open the student data file named **U6A3-RentalCars**.

2  Create a new table in Design view.

3  Define the table to have the following fields and data types:

| Field Name | Data Type |
|------------|-----------|
| ID | Number |
| CarYear | Number |
| Make | Short Text |
| Model | Short Text |
| Color | Short Text |
| Mileage | Number |

4  Make the *ID* field the primary key.

5  Save the table, typing *Cars* as the table name.

6  Enter the following records in the Cars table:

| ID | CarYear | Make | Model | Color | Mileage |
|----|---------|------|-------|-------|---------|
| 345 | 2019 | Ford | Fiesta | Red | 37295 |
| 781 | 2019 | Ford | Fiesta | Blue | 12000 |
| 237 | 2020 | Honda | Civic | Brown | 10000 |
| 861 | 2018 | Nissan | Maxima | White | 50000 |

7  Sort the records by car year in ascending order.

8  Save and close the table.

9  Use the Form button to create a form based on the Cars table.

10  Use the Logo button to insert the student data file **U6A3-Car** in the form header.

11  AutoFit the logo.

12  Save the form, naming it *Cars*.

13  Use the Cars form in Form view to enter the following records in the database:

| ID | CarYear | Make | Model | Color | Mileage |
|----|---------|------|-------|-------|---------|
| 112 | 2019 | Honda | Civic | Black | 12000 |
| 134 | 2020 | Chevrolet | Cruze | Black | 8550 |
| 654 | 2020 | Chevrolet | Cruze | White | 2200 |

14  Print the Cars form or submit the completed form as directed by your instructor. Close the form.

15  Open the Cars table and filter the data to display 2019 cars.

16  Print the Cars table or submit the filtered table as directed by your instructor.

17  Remove the filter, save the table, and then close the table.

18  Open the Relationships window and create a one-to-many relationship between the *ID* field in the Cars and Reservations tables. Click the *Enforce Referential Integrity* option. Close the Relationships window.

19  Use the Query Design button to create a query of all reservations. Add the Cars table and the Reservations table to the query. Display the *ReservationNumber*, *CustomerLastName*, *CustomerFirstName*, and *Model* fields, in that order, in the query. Sort the query by *CustomerLastName* in ascending order.

20  Run the query.

21  Save the query, typing *CustomerReservations* as the query name.

22  Print the CustomerReservations query or submit the query result as directed by your instructor. Close the query.

23  Use the Report button to create a report based on the CustomersReservations query.

24  Group the report by the *CustomerLastName* field. **Hint:** *Click the Group & Sort button in the Grouping & Totals group on the Report Layout Tools Design tab, click the Add a group button, and then click the* CustomerLastName *field.*

25  Use the Report Layout Tools Page Setup tab to change the print orientation to landscape.

26  AutoFit the *Record Count* cell.

27  Edit the Report Header to read *Customer Reservations*. **Hint:** *Click the Report Header, open the Property Sheet, and then edit the Caption property.*

28  Save the report, typing *CustomerReservations* as the report name.

29  Print the CustomerReservations report or submit the completed report as directed by your instructor. Close the report.

30  Close the database and submit the completed file as directed by your instructor.

*Completed Assessment 3, Cars Form*

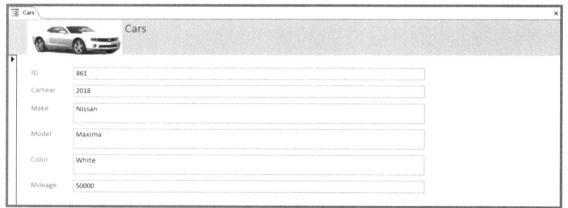

*Completed Assessment 3, Filtered 2019 Cars Table*

### *Completed Assessment 3, CustomerReservations Query*

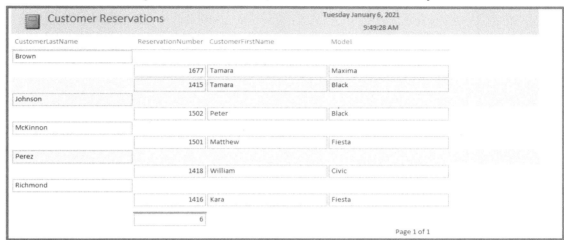

### *Completed Assessment 3, CustomerReservations Report*

| Customer Reservations | | | Tuesday January 6, 2021 |
| --- | --- | --- | --- |
| | | | 9:49:28 AM |

| CustomerLastName | ReservationNumber | CustomerFirstName | Model |
| --- | --- | --- | --- |
| Brown | | | |
| | 1677 | Tamara | Maxima |
| | 1415 | Tamara | Black |
| Johnson | | | |
| | 1502 | Peter | Black |
| McKinnon | | | |
| | 1501 | Matthew | Fiesta |
| Perez | | | |
| | 1418 | William | Civic |
| Richmond | | | |
| | 1416 | Kara | Fiesta |
| | 6 | | |

Page 1 of 1

# UNIT 7

# PowerPoint Review and Assessment

Chapter 1   **Creating a Presentation**

Chapter 2   **Adding Media Elements and Effects**

Chapter 3   **Customizing a Slide Show**

Chapter 4   **Completing, Running, and Sharing Your Show**

        **Unit 7 Skills Assessment**

The online course includes additional review and assessment resources.

# PowerPoint Review and Assessment

## Chapter 1 **Creating a Presentation**

### Study Quiz

*Online courseware includes a Study Quiz.*

### Features Review

*Online courseware includes a Features Review consisting of 10 multiple-choice questions to help reinforce your understanding of the chapter content.*

### Skills Review 1 **Traveling Safely with a Dog**

**Skills**    **CH1:** Open PowerPoint and insert a slide, enter text on slides, add notes, apply a layout and run a slide show, apply a theme, and organize slides using the Slide Sorter feature

**Scenario**    You have been asked to update a presentation used to advise pet owners about safe practices when traveling with a pet. Edit the file provided to improve the presentation.

**Steps**

1. Open the student data file named **C1R1-Travel** and save the file as **C1R1-Travel-Lastname**, but replace *Lastname* with your last name.

2. Type your name in the subtitle placeholder on the title slide.

3. Apply the Picture with Caption layout to Slide 4, *Relax and Have Fun*.

4. Add the following speaker note to Slide 4, *Relax and Have Fun*:
   If you plan carefully, a trip with a pet can be fun and rewarding.

5. At the end of the presentation, insert a new slide with the Title and Content layout.
   a. Type Accommodations as the slide title.
   b. Type the following content as three bullet points:
      Review pet policies, such as not allowing dogs to be left alone in the room.
      Use white noise to help muffle sounds in the hallway and keep your dog quiet.
      Help your dog soothe himself by providing a bedtime chew stick or favorite toy.

6. Apply the Crop theme, and then apply the fourth variant.

7. Review the slide order and reorganize the slides so they appear in the following sequence:
   Slide 1: *Travel Safely with Your Dog*
   Slide 2: *Accommodations*
   Slide 3: *Medical*
   Slide 4: *Vehicle*
   Slide 5: *Relax and Have Fun*

8. Save the file.

9. Run the presentation. ***Hint:*** *Click the Slide Show tab, and then click the From Beginning button.*

10. Print or submit the completed file as directed by your instructor.

*Completed Review 1*

 ## Skills Review 2 **Creating Effective Presentations**

**Skills**  **CH1:** Open PowerPoint and insert a slide, enter text on slides, add notes, apply a layout and run a slide show, and apply a theme

**Scenario**  You are working on a presentation that will be delivered to your company's sales reps at the national sales meeting. This presentation will remind the reps how to make interesting and engaging presentations.

**Steps**

1  Open the student data file named **C1R2-EffectivePresentations** and save the file as **C1R2-EffectivePresentations-Lastname**, but replace *Lastname* with your last name.

2  Type your name in the subtitle placeholder on the title slide.

3  Insert a new Title and Content slide after Slide 2. Type the title Content and add the following content as four bullet points:
      Title slide
      Objectives
      Content
      Ending

4 Apply the Banded theme to the presentation.

5 Apply the fourth variant to the presentation.

6 Add the following speaker note to Slide 2, *Plan*:
It is important to take the time to plan out your presentation before sitting down at your computer.

7 Save the presentation.

8 Run the presentation.

9 Print or submit the completed file as directed by your instructor.

*Completed Review 2*

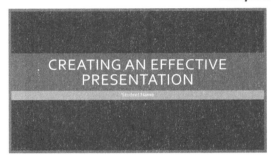

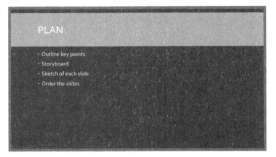

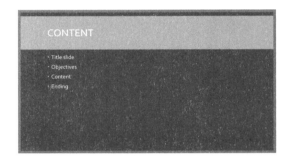

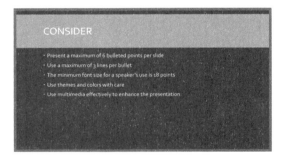

## Skills Review 3   **Telling Others about Therapy Cats**

**Skills**      **CH1:** Enter text on slides, add notes, apply a layout and run a slide show, apply a theme; and organize slides using the Slide Sorter feature

**Scenario**   Therapy animals visit people who are sick or disabled to help them feel better. A colleague has drafted a presentation about two certified therapy cats for you to use in telling others about the program. Update and customize the presentation by making it more eye-catching and adding speaker notes.

**Steps**

1  Open the student data file named **C1R3-CatsWork** and save the file as **C1R3-CatsWork-Lastname**, but replace *Lastname* with your last name.

2  Place the slides into the correct sequence:
   Slide 1: *Cats at Work*
   Slide 2: *Topics*
   Slide 3: *Growing Up*
   Slide 4: *Pet Therapy*
   Slide 5: *Certified Therapy Animals, Delta Society*
   Slide 6: *Certifying Gerald and Marcel Ensures That They Keep Calm*
   Slide 7: *Story of a Visit*
   Slide 8: *Retirement*

3  Type your name in the subtitle placeholder on the title slide.

4  Update Slide 5, *Certified Therapy Animals, Delta Society* as follows:
   a.  Apply the Comparison layout.
   b.  In the left column, type Dogs as the column heading. In the content placeholder below the heading, type the following bullets:
   Tested every 2 years
   On personality and demeanor
   On obedience
   c.  In the right column, type Cats as the column heading. In the content placeholder below the heading, type the following bullets:
   Tested every 2 years
   On personality and demeanor
   Not on obedience because cats rarely respond to obedience commands

5  Add the following speaker notes to Slide 5, *Certified Therapy Animals*:
   Not every animal will earn certification. The animal must be patient and have the necessary skills.

6  Add a sentence to the end of the speaker notes for Slide 6, *Certifying Gerald and Marcel*:
   They were patient and loving.

7  Apply the Ion theme to the presentation. Do not apply a variant.

8  Save the file.

9  Run the presentation.

10  Print or submit the completed file as directed by your instructor.

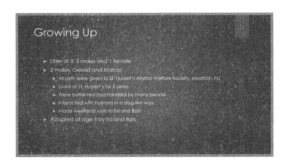

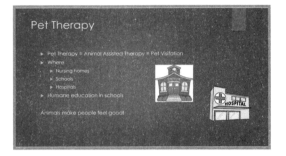

## Chapter 2 **Adding Media Elements and Effects**

### Study Quiz

*Online courseware includes a Study Quiz.*

### Features Review

*Online courseware includes a Features Review consisting of 10 multiple-choice questions to help reinforce your understanding of the chapter content.*

### Skills Review 1  **Adding Media to a Presentation on Car Racing**

**Skills**  **CH1:** Enter text and apply a theme **CH2:** Insert and position a picture, format a picture, insert a 3D model, add transitions, add a sound effect to a transition, and add animations

**Scenario**  Add interest to a presentation of historical points about car racing by inserting, sizing, and positioning an image; adding and animating a 3D model; adding transitions; and adding a sound effect to a transition.

**Steps**

1  Open the student data file named **C2R1-CarRacing** and save the file as **C2R1-CarRacing-Lastname**, but replace *Lastname* with your last name.

2  On Slide 1, type your name in the subtitle placeholder.

3  On Slide 1, make the following modifications:
   a.  Insert the 3D model shown in the screen capture using the *From Online Sources* option and *Cars* as the search criteria. **Hint:** *Scroll to find the green car that has the number 15 on the hood.*
   b.  Size the 3D model to a height of 1.1 inches and a width of 2.31 inches. Next, move the 3D model to the horizontal position 10.77 inches from the top left corner and to the vertical position 5.66 inches from the top left corner. **Hint:** *Use the* Size *options and* Position *options in the* Size & Properties *section of the Format 3D Model task pane.*
   c.  Close the Format 3D Model task pane.

4  Add the Arrive animation to the 3D model. **Hint:** *Select the 3D model, click the Animations tab, and then apply the Arrive animation.*

5  Apply the Gallery theme to the presentation.

6  Add the Pan transition to all of the slides.

7  On Slide 1, use the Transitions tab to add the Whoosh sound. Set the duration to 1.50.

8  On Slide 6, insert the student data file named **C2R1-RaceCar2** (a picture file) in the content placeholder at the right side of the slide. Apply the Bevel Rectangle picture style.

9  On Slide 7, select the website URL (https://GL19.ParadigmEducation.com/Nascar) and change the font to Arial and the font size to 28 point. With the URL still selected, click the Change Case button in the Font group on the Home tab and click the *lowercase* option.

10  Save the presentation.

11  Preview the presentation.

12  Print or submit the completed file as directed by your instructor.

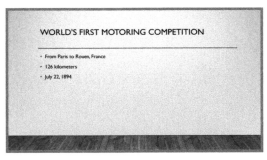

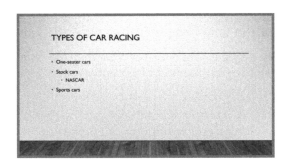

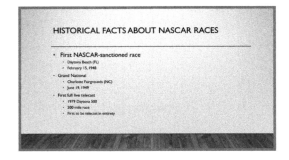

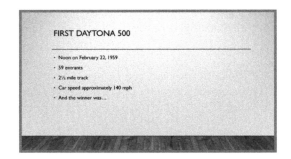

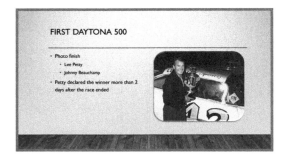

## Skills Review 2  **Adding Media to a Presentation about Donny**

**Skills**  **CH1:** Enter text, apply a layout, and apply a theme **CH2:** Insert and position a picture, format a picture, add transitions, and insert a video

**Scenario**  Enhance a presentation about the adoption of a newborn kitten by adding a theme, modifying the background, repositioning a picture, and adding a video.

**Steps**

1  Open the student data file named **C2R2-Donny** and save it as **C2R2-Donny-Lastname**, but replace *Lastname* with your last name.

2  In Slide 1, type your name in the subtitle placeholder.

3  Apply the Retrospect theme and then apply the second color variant.

4  On Slide 1, move the picture to the horizontal position 9.20 inches from the top left corner and to the vertical position 0.54" from the top left corner. ***Hint:*** *Use the* Position *options in the* Size & Properties *section of the Format Picture task pane.*

5  On Slide 4, apply the Rounded Diagonal Corner, White picture style to the image.

6  On Slide 8, change the layout to Comparison, and then make the following additional changes:
   a.  In the heading text box on the left, type Donny likes….
   b.  In the heading text box on the right, type See Donny doing some tricks!. *Note that the placeholder text in the heading text box is in all capital letters. This indicates that the Retrospect theme will automatically format the replacement text you type in the all caps style.*
   c.  In the content placeholder on the right, insert the student data file named **C2R2-Donny8Tricks**, which is a video file. ***Hint:*** *Use the* Video on My PC *option in the Video drop-down list in the Media group on the Insert tab.* Set the video to play automatically.

7  Add the Page Curl transition to all of the slides.

8  Save the presentation.

9  Preview the presentation. Ensure that the video plays automatically.

10  Print or submit the completed file as directed by your instructor.

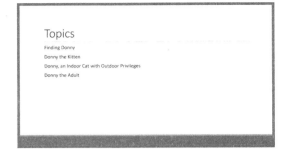

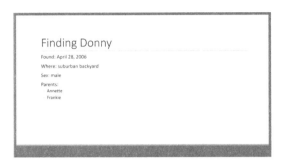

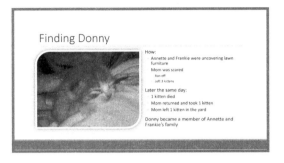

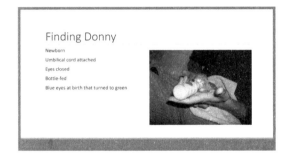

## Skills Review 3  Adding More Media to Your Scuba Presentation

**Skills**  **CH1:** Enter text, and apply a theme **CH2:** Insert a 3D model, add a Morph transition to a 3D model, add transitions, and add a sound effect to a transition

**Scenario**  You are a scuba instructor and have created a presentation of scuba photographs that you are going to show to your students. First, enhance the scuba presentation by adding a 3D model, transitions, and sound effects.

**Steps**

1  Open the student data file named **C2R3-Scuba** and save the file as **C2R3-Scuba-Lastname**, but replace *Lastname* with your last name.

2  On Slide 1, replace *Name* with your first and last name.

3  Apply the Metropolitan theme.

4  Add the Reveal transition to Slide 1.

5  Add the Breeze sound to the slide transition on Slide 1.

6  On Slide 1, make the following modifications:

    a. Insert the 3D model shown in the screen capture using the *From Online Sources* option and *scuba* as the search criteria.

    b. Move the 3D model to the horizontal position 8.45 inches from the top left corner and to the vertical position 1.00 inches from the top left corner. **Hint:** *Use the* Position *options in the* Size & Properties *section of the Format 3D Model task pane.*

    c. Close the Format 3D Model task pane.

    d. Change the 3D Model view to the *Below Front* option.

7  Duplicate Slide 1.

8  On Slide 2, change the 3D Model view to the *Below Back* option.

9  Add the Morph transition to Slide 2.

10  Save the presentation.

11  Preview the presentation.

12  Print or submit the completed file as directed by your instructor.

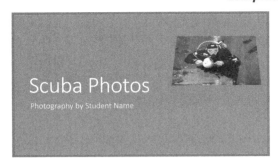

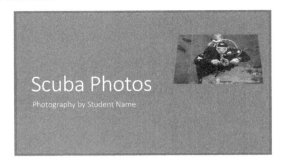

## Chapter 3 **Customizing a Slide Show**

### Study Quiz

*Online courseware includes a Study Quiz.*

### Features Review

*Online courseware includes a Features Review consisting of 10 multiple-choice questions to help reinforce your understanding of the chapter content.*

### Skills Review 1  **Formatting a Presentation on US Presidents**

**Skills**    **CH1:** Enter text on slides **CH3:** Change the theme colors, add a footer, format text in Slide Master view, and change the indent level

**Scenario**  Each student in your history class will deliver a presentation on four presidents of the United States. You have been assigned the first four presidents. Update the presentation by adding a theme, modifying colors and fonts, and adding a footer.

**Steps**

1 Open the student data file named **C3R1-Presidents** and save the file as **C3R1-Presidents-Lastname**, but replace *Lastname* with your last name.

2 On Slide 1, insert a new line after the dates *1789-1817* in the subtitle placeholder and then type your name on the new line.

3 Change the theme colors to the *Blue II* option.

4 Add to all presentation slides a footer that contains the text Source: https://www. whitehouse.gov/1600/Presidents. Do not show the footer on the title slide.

5 Modify the slide master as follows:
   Apply the Bauhaus 93 font to the text in the title placeholder on all slides. ***Hint:*** *Click the top thumbnail in the slide thumbnails pane (you may need to scroll up), and then click in the title placeholder text in the slide pane before making changes.*

6 Close Slide Master view and return to Normal view.

7 On Slide 5, increase the indent level of the last two bulleted items.

8 Save the presentation.

9 Preview the presentation.

10 Print or submit the completed file as directed by your instructor.

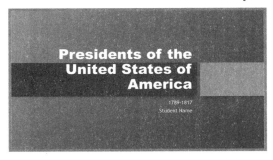
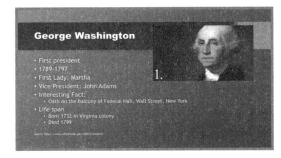
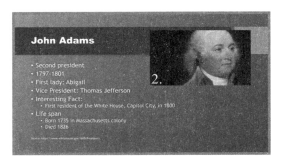
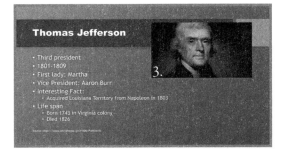
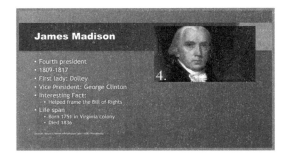

 ## Skills Review 2  **Enhancing a Sales Presentation**

**Skills**  **CH1:** Enter text on slides **CH3:** Insert a logo, add a footer, change the indent level, and add an action button

**Scenario**  Enhance a sales presentation by inserting a graphic in the slide master and then making adjustments to the graphic that will appear on all slides. You also need to add a footer, indent text, and add an action button.

**Steps**

1  Open the student data file named **C3R2-Sales** and save the file as **C3R2-Sales-Lastname**, but replace *Lastname* with your last name.

2  In Slide 1, type your name in the subtitle placeholder.

3  In Slide Master view, insert the **C3R2-Logo** logo on all of the slides in the presentation. *Hint: Scroll to the top of the slide thumbnails pane and then click the slide master.*
   a.  Change the width of the logo to 1.2".
   b.  Position the logo horizontally 0.1" from the top left corner and vertically 0.1" from the top left corner.
   c. Close Slide Master view.

4  Insert a footer with the slide number on all slides except the title slide.

**5** Increase the indent level of the last bullet point on Slide 3.

**6** On Slide 3, insert the Action Button: Return action button.

    a. Draw the button in the bottom right corner of the slide. Size the action button to have a height of 0.75" and a width of 0.67". ***Hint:*** *Click the Action button, click the Drawing Tools Format tab, and then use options in the Size group to set the height and width.*

    b. Accept the *Hyperlink to: Last Slide Viewed* action.

    c. With the action button selected, click the Drawing Tools Format tab and change the shape style to the *Colored Fill - Turquoise, Accent 1* option.

**7** Save the presentation.

**8** Preview the presentation and test the action button.

**9** Print or submit the completed file as directed by your instructor.

***Completed Review 2***

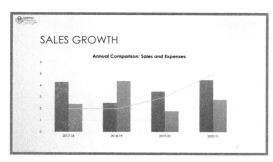

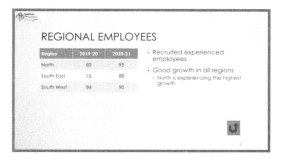

## Skills Review 3   **Improving an Animal Shelter Presentation**

**Skills**     **CH1:** Enter text on slides **CH3:** Change the theme colors, add a footer, format text in Slide Master view, change the indent level, and add an action button

**Scenario**   You are preparing a presentation about pet adoption. Improve the presentation by adding a theme and a footer.

**Steps**

**1** Open the student data file named **C3R3-Shelter** and save the file as **C3R3-Shelter-Lastname**, but replace *Lastname* with your last name.

**2** Change the theme colors to the *Paper* option.

**3** Change the theme font to the *Corbel* option.

**4** On all slides except the title slide, insert a footer that includes your name and the slide number.

5   Modify the Banded slide master as follows:
    a.  In the content placeholder, select the *Edit Master text styles* placeholder text, and then change the font color to Orange, Accent 2.
    b.  Close Slide Master view and return to Normal view.

6   On Slide 6, increase the indent level of the last three bulleted items.

7   Research and find a link to a local animal shelter. On Slide 8, add the Action Button: Get Information action button to the bottom left corner of the slide. Size the action button to have a height of 0.6" and a width of 0.67". **Hint**: *Click the Action button, click the Drawing Tools Format tab, and then use options in the Size group to set the height and width. Create a hyperlink to the URL of your local animal shelter.*

8   Save the presentation.

9   Preview the presentation and test the action button.

10  Print or submit the completed file as directed by your instructor.

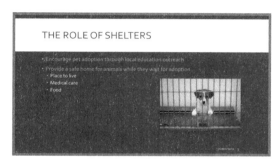

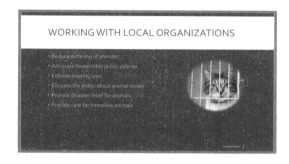

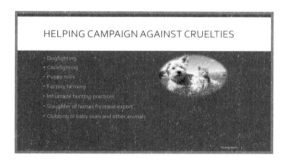

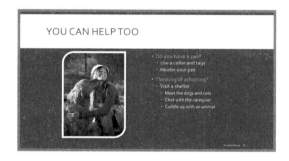

PowerPoint Review and Assessment

## Chapter 4
## Completing, Running, and Sharing Your Show

 ### Study Quiz

*Online courseware includes a Study Quiz.*

 ### Features Review

*Online courseware includes a Features Review consisting of 10 multiple-choice questions to help reinforce your understanding of the chapter content.*

 ### Skills Review 1  **Completing a Presentation on Creating a Business Plan**

**Skills**  **CH1:** Enter text on slides **CH3:** Add a footer **CH4:** Check spelling, run a show for an audience, present online, and use the Zoom feature

**Scenario**  You are completing a presentation on creating a business plan. As the final steps in your preparation, review the content for spelling errors and add a footer.

**Steps**

1  Open the student data file named **C4R1-BusinessPlan** and save the file as **C4R1-BusinessPlan-Lastname**, but replace *Lastname* with your last name.

2  On Slide 1 (the title slide), type your name in the subtitle placeholder.

3  On all slides except the title slide, insert a footer displaying the slide number and the text *Creating a Business Plan*.

4  Check the spelling of the slide content and correct any errors you find. Check your corrections against the Completed Review 1 slides shown below.

5  Save the file.

6  Preview the presentation.

7  Use the Zoom feature to insert a Summary Zoom slide containing all of the slides in the presentation. ***Note:*** *PowerPoint automatically adjusts slide numbers when a Summary Zoom slide is added to the presentation. If you do not want the Summary Zoom slide to count as Slide 1, click the Slide Size button in the Customize group on the Design tab and then click the* Custom Slide Size *option. In the Slide Size dialog box, change the value in the* Number slides from *option box to 0.*

8  Present online as directed by your instructor.

9  Print or submit the completed file as directed by your instructor.

***Completed Review 1***

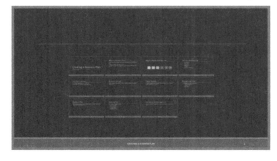

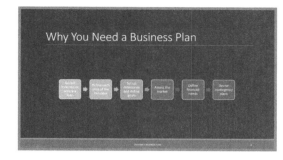

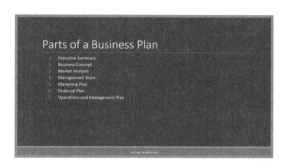

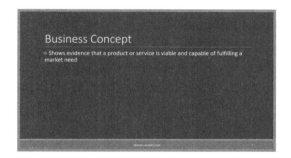

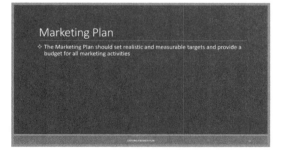

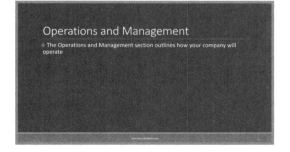

PowerPoint Review and Assessment

## Skills Review 2  Printing Handouts and Notes for a Presentation on Creating a Business Plan

**Skills**  **CH1:** Enter text on slides **CH4:** Print speaker notes with a header

**Scenario**  You are preparing to deliver your business plan presentation. Print handouts for the audience and print notes pages that you can use as a guide while presenting.

**Steps**

1  Open **C4R1-BusinessPlan-Lastname**, the file you saved in Skills Review 1, and save it as **C4R2-BusinessPlan-Lastname**, but replace *Lastname* with your last name.

2  Use the Edit Header & Footer link in the Print backstage area to add a header and a footer to all notes and handouts pages as follows:
   a.  Include a date that will update automatically.
   b.  Include a page number.
   c.  Include a header, typing your name in the *Header* text box.

3  Delete all Sections and Slide 1 (the Summary Zoom slide). ***Hint:*** *Right-click the Summary Section section in the slide thumbnail pane and then click* Remove All Sections *in the pop-up menu. Next, right click Slide 1 in the slide thumbnail pane, and then click* Delete Slide *in the pop-up menu.*

4  Save the file.

*Check with your instructor about printing before completing Steps 5 and 6.*

5  Print one set of handouts for your audience, including all the slides in the presentation, with three slides per page.

6  Print one set of notes pages, including all the slides in the presentation, to use as talking points during delivery of the presentation.

7  Submit both sets of printouts as directed by your instructor.

### *Completed Review 2, Handouts*

Skills Review 3  **Setting Up a Presentation on Creating a Business Plan**

**Skills**    **CH2:** Add transitions **CH4:** Run a show for an audience, rehearse timings, and set up a show using timings

**Scenario**  You decide to set timings so the Creating a Business Plan slide show can run without a speaker present.

**Steps**

1   Open **C4R2-BusinessPlan-Lastname**, the file you saved in the previous exercise, and save the file as **C4R3-BusinessPlan-Lastname**, but replace *Lastname* with your last name.

2   Add the Reveal transition to all slides in the presentation.

3   Complete Option 1 or Option 2, and then complete the optional extension activity as directed by your instructor.
    a.  **Option 1:** Set the timings for the slides in the presentation as follows:
        Slide 1: 0:00:04
        Slide 2: 0:00:04
        Slide 3: 0:00:06
        Slide 4: 0:00:08
        Slide 5: 0:00:07
        Slide 6: 0:00:05
        Slide 7: 0:00:05
        Slide 8: 0:00:05
        Slide 9: 0:00:05
        Slide 10: 0:00:05
        Slide 11: 0:00:05
    b.  **Option 2:** Add customized timings to all slides in the presentation using the Rehearse Timings button on the Slide Show tab. ***Hint:*** *It is difficult to determine how long each slide should appear. To achieve realistic timings, read every line on the slide slowly, as if you were seeing it for the first time; spend a moment looking at each of the images on the slide; and then move to the next slide.*
    c.  **Optional extension activity:** Record a narration of the slide's notes and set the timing to match the length of the narration. ***Hint:*** *Review the Taking It Further: Recording a Slide Show feature in Skill 4 of this chapter. Find a quiet place to record the narration. Ask for a microphone if necessary. Speak slowly and give the viewer enough time to look at the images on each slide before moving to the next slide.*

4   Set up the slide show to play automatically when browsed at a kiosk.

5   Save the file.

6   Preview the presentation.

7   Print or submit the completed file as directed by your instructor.

*Completed Review 3 Option 1, Slide Sorter View*

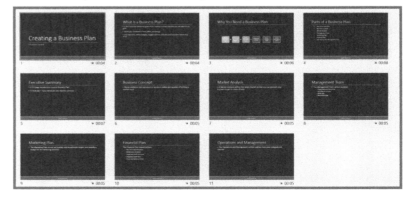

# PowerPoint Review and Assessment

## Unit 7 Microsoft PowerPoint

 **Skills Assessment 1** **Pet Presentation for Middle School Students**

**Skills** **CH1:** Open PowerPoint and insert a slide, enter text on slides, add notes, and apply a theme **CH2:** Insert and position a picture, format a picture, add transitions, add animations, and choose animation effects **CH3:** Change the theme colors, add a footer, and format text in Slide Master view **CH4:** Check spelling, print speaker notes with a header, present online, and use the Zoom feature

**Scenario** You work for a veterinarian who has been asked to present a workshop about pets at the local middle school. You decide to create a slide presentation to share engaging pictures and basic information about some healthy patients. You enhance the presentation to keep the middle school students interested. You are not able to be present at the school, so you arrange to present online. You also print speaker notes for you to refer to during the presentation.

**Steps**

1 Open the student data file named **U7A1-PetsPlay** and save the file as **U7A1-PetsPlay-Lastname**, but replace *Lastname* with your last name.

2 In Slide 1, type your name in the subtitle placeholder.

3 Apply the Berlin theme to all slides. Do not apply a variant.

4 Change the theme colors to the *Median* option.

5 Open Slide Master view. In all slides that use the Picture with Caption layout (Slides 6, 10, 14, and 18), change the font size for the text in the left content box to 24 points. Close Slide Master view. ***Hint:*** *Hover over any layout master thumbnail to display a ScreenTip with the name of the layout.*

6 Add the Split transition and *Vertical In* effect option to all slides.

7 Add a picture to each of the four section header slides as described below, using the student data files provided. Change the height of each image to 4". Do not adjust the width. Place each image in the left center of the slide at the horizontal position 0.75" from the top left corner and the vertical position 1.6 inches from the top left corner.
   a. Slide 3: **U7A1-Izzie**
   b. Slide 7: **U7A1-Riley**
   c. Slide 11: **U7A1-Hannah**
   d. Slide 15: **U7A1-Mollie**

8 Add the following entrance and emphasis animations. Set each animation to start after the previous animation is done.
   a. Slide 3 image: Float In animation and *Float Up* effect option
   b. Slide 7 image: Zoom animation and *Slide Center* effect option
   c. Slide 11 image: Grow & Turn animation
   d. Slide 15 image: Grow/Shrink animation and *Larger* effect option

9 On all slides except the title slide, insert a footer that displays the text *Cats and Dogs at Play* and the slide number.

10 Add a header to the notes and handouts pages. Type your name in the *Header* text box and add the page number.

11 Type the following speaker notes in the notes pane:
   a. **Slide 2:** Meet some amazing pets. Izzie, Riley, and Mollie are funny and interesting dogs. Hannah is a remarkable cat.
   b. **Slide 16:** Lhasa Apso dogs were raised by Tibetan monks as guard dogs. They have a fierce bark even though they are small.

12 Check the presentation for spelling errors and correct any errors you find.

13 In the slide thumbnails pane, right-click between Slide 2 and Slide 3, and then click *Add Section* on the pop-up menu to add an *Untitled Section*. In the Rename dialog box, type Izzie, and then click the Rename button.

14 Add sections between the following slides by repeating Step 13:
   a. Add a section between Slides 6 and 7. Rename the section Riley.
   b. Add a section between Slides 10 and 11. Rename the section Hannah.
   c. Add a section between Slides 14 and 15. Rename the section Mollie.

15 Insert a Summary Zoom slide. In the Insert Summary Zoom dialog box, the slides at the beginning of each section are automatically selected (Slides 3, 7, 11, and 15). Click the Insert button to accept the selected sections. The Summary Zoom slide is inserted before the first section (Slide 3).

16 Switch to Slide Sorter view. Notice how the presentation is organized into sections.

17 Preview the presentation. Notice how the section zoom allows you flexibility to view the sections in any order.

18 Save the file.

19 Present the presentation online as directed by your instructor.

*Check with your instructor before completing Step 20.*

20 Print one copy each of the notes pages for Slides 2 and 17. **Hint:** *Click the* Print All Slides *option box in the* Settings *category, click the* Custom Range *option in the drop-down list, and then type* 2, 17 *in the* Slides *text box.*

## Completed Assessment 1, Step 16

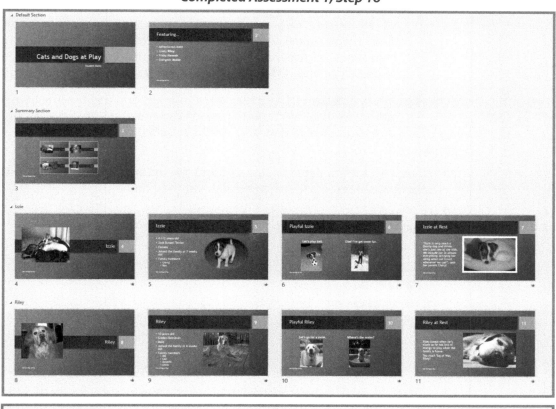

## Completed Assessment 1, Step 20

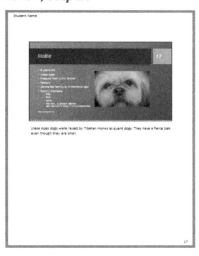

## Skills Assessment 2 **Arithmetic Flash Cards**

**Skills** **CH1:** Enter text on slides, apply a layout and run a slide show, apply a theme, and organize slides using the Slide Sorter feature **CH2:** Insert a 3D model, add transitions, add animations, and choose animation effects **CH3:** Format text in Slide Master view **CH4:** Run a show for an audience, and present online

**Scenario** Your neighbor's child is learning arithmetic and needs some help. Create an arithmetic flash card tutorial using PowerPoint. Make it interesting and fun as well as educational so that your neighbor's child practices often.

**Steps**

1  Open the student data file named **U7A2-FlashCards** and save it as **U7A2-FlashCards-Lastname**, but replace *Lastname* with your last name.

2  Use the Slide Sorter to place the slides in the following order:
   a. Slide 1: *Flash Cards*
   b. Slide 2: *Addition*
   c. Slide 3: *Subtraction*
   d. Slide 4: *Multiplication*
   e. Slide 5: *Division*
   f. Slide 6: *Exponentiation*
   g. Slide 7: *Interpreting Your Score*

3  Switch to Normal view. In Slide 1, type your name in the subtitle placeholder.

4  Open Slide Master view. You will stay in Slide Master view for Steps 5 through 8.

5  In the slide thumbnails pane, click the Comparison Layout thumbnail. In the slide pane, modify the left and right content placeholders (displaying bulleted text) as described below. ***Hint:*** *You can select and modify each placeholder separately or modify both placeholders at the same time. To modify the placeholders separately, click the left placeholder, complete Steps 5a through 5d, click the right placeholder, and then complete Steps 5a through 5d again. To modify both content placeholders at the same time, select both placeholders using the Click, Shift-Click method—click one, hold down the Shift key while you click the other, and then release the Shift key—and then complete Steps 5a through 5d.*
   a. Turn off bullets. ***Hint:*** *Click the Bullets button in the Paragraph group on the Home tab.*
   b. Center the text.
   c. Middle-align the text. ***Hint:*** *Click the Align Text button in the Paragraph group on the Home tab, and then click the* Middle *option in the drop-down list.*
   d. Change the font size to 40 points.

6  With the Comparison Layout slide master still selected, center the text in the left and right caption placeholders (directly above the content placeholders).

7  Modify the left caption and content placeholders as described below, using commands in the Shape Styles group on the Drawing Tools Format tab:
   a. Apply the theme color Black, Text 1 to the shape outline.
   b. Apply the theme color Blue, Accent 5, Lighter 40% to the shape fill.

8  Modify the right caption and content placeholders as described below, using commands in the Shape Styles group on the Drawing Tools Format tab:
   a. Apply the theme color Black, Text 1 to the shape outline.
   b. Apply the theme color Green, Accent 6, Lighter 40% to the shape fill.

9  Return to Normal view.

10  In Slides 1 and 7 (the title and final slides), apply the Retrospect theme, and select the second variant (green). **Hint:** *Select the indicated slides in the slide thumbnails pane, right-click the* Retrospect *theme, and then click* Apply to Selected Slides.

11  On Slide 1, insert a 3D model from an online source as follows:
   a.  Type math in the search box and insert the question mark 3D model, as shown in the completed slides, or a similar 3D model.
   b.  Change the size of the 3D model to 2.5" high.
   c.  Position the 3D model at the horizontal position 7.0" from the top left corner and the vertical position 2.0" from the top left corner.
   d.  Apply the Jump & Turn animation to the 3D model.

12  Add transitions as follows:
   a.  Slide 1: Fade transition, *Smoothly* effect option
   b.  Slides 2–6: Cover transition, *From Bottom-Right* effect option
   c.  Slide 7: Shape transition, *Circle* effect option

13  Add animations as follows:
   a.  Open Slide Master view.
   b.  In the slide thumbnails pane, click the Comparison Layout thumbnail. **Hint:** *Scroll up and locate the first* Comparison *layout, which is the same layout that you modified in Steps 5 through 8 of this assessment.*
   c.  Select the right caption and content placeholders using the Click, Shift-Click method.
   d.  Apply the Appear animation and the *As One Object* effect option.
   e.  Close Slide Master view.

14  Save the file.

15  Run the presentation to preview your work.

16  View the presentation in Slide Sorter view.

17  Print or submit the completed file as directed by your instructor.

18  **Optional extension activity:** Run the slide show manually for an audience or present the slide show online. If you present online, ask your instructor where to send the email link.

*Completed Assessment 2, Step 16*

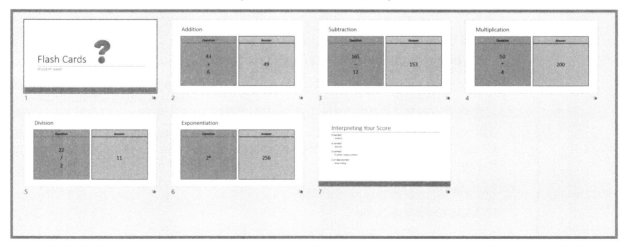

Skills Assessment 3 **Business Proposal Presentation**

**Skills** **CH1:** Open PowerPoint and insert a slide, enter text on slides, add notes, apply a layout and run a slide show, and apply a theme **CH2:** Insert and position a picture, format a picture, insert a 3D model, add transitions, insert a video, add a sound effect to a transition, add animations, and choose animation effects **CH3:** Insert a logo, add a footer, and format text in Slide Master view **CH4:** Collaborate on a slide show, check spelling, run a show for an audience, rehearse timings, set up a show to run using timings, print speaker notes with a header, and present online

**Scenario** Create an engaging presentation that pitches a business idea. The presentation audience is potential investors. Be sure to include the business name, organizational structure, sales forecast, advertising plan, target market, and why you think the business can be successful. You may want to collaborate with a classmate on the presentation. Share the presentation as specified by your instructor.

**Steps**

1 Create a new PowerPoint presentation or search for an appropriate template. Save it as **U7A3-Business-Lastname**, but replace *Lastname* with your last name.

2 Create the presentation according to the following specifications:

- Include at least five, but not more than eight, slides.

- At least three slides should contain pictures, a video, or a 3D model. You may also want to include a chart, table, or SmartArt. Be sure to include the source of each object.

- Use the Title Slide layout on Slide 1 and use two additional layouts on other slides.

- Apply a theme.

- Apply transitions to two or more slides.

- Add one appropriate sound to play during a transition.

- Animate the images, 3D model, and/or text on two or more slides.

- In all slides except the title slide, add a footer that includes an automatically updating date, your name, and the slide number.

- On the slide master, make a modification to the title font that will affect all slides.

- Include speaker notes that can be used if you are asked to deliver the presentation.

- Set timings that are appropriate for individuals viewing the slide show without a speaker.

- **Optional extension activity:** Add both narration and timings.

3 Ensure your slides are set to automatically advance using the timings you have added.

4 Check your spelling in the slides and the notes.

5 Ask your instructor whether you will be sharing the presentation online or delivering it in class. If you are to deliver the presentation in class, make the required adjustments so the slides advance manually.

6 Save the file.

7 Preview the presentation.

8 Print or submit the completed file as directed by your instructor.

# UNIT **8**

## Integrating Office Applications Review and Assessment

 The online course includes additional review and assessment resources.

 **Study Quiz**

*Online courseware includes a Study Quiz.*

## Unit 8 Integrating Office Applications

**Skills Assessment** **An Electronic Menu and Ordering System for a Restaurant**

**Skills**     Skills used will vary depending on choices you make. Requirements include use of Word, Excel, Access, and PowerPoint, as well as integration of Access with Excel.

**Scenario**     You manage a neighborhood restaurant, and lately, several customers have complained that the service is very slow. The restaurant staff are often busy, and customers have to wait long periods of time to get a menu and place an order. You meet with the owner of the restaurant to express your concern about this issue, and he asks you to help him explore options for setting up an electronic menu and ordering system. You agree to do the following:

- **Part A:** Create a PowerPoint presentation that explains the benefits of using an electronic menu and ordering system.
- **Part B:** Use the Mail Merge feature in Word to create personalized letters asking three vendors who specialize in electronic menu and ordering technology for more information about their product.
- **Part C:** Create an Access database that contains a table of menu items by name, description, and price, and that also contains an order query.
- **Part D:** Create an Excel workbook that generates a bill for an order and compares the costs of the items in the bill.
- **Part E:** Submit the seven project files to your instructor.

**Steps, Part A**

Go online and research the benefits of using an electronic menu and ordering system. Create a PowerPoint presentation that you can deliver, in person, to explain the benefits to the restaurant owner. Create handouts by exporting the presentation to Word.

1   Start with a new, blank presentation or a PowerPoint template.

2   Include six to eight slides total.

3   Use the Title Slide layout for the first slide.

4   For the slides following the title slide:
   a.  Use at least two different slide layouts.
   b.  In at least four slides, insert one or more types of media (e.g., images, 3D models, SmartArt diagrams); each object should include a caption that indicates its source.
   c.  Include text on every slide, including the slide title.
   d.  Include at least two different transitions within the presentation.
   e.  In three slides, animate one or more objects. Each animation should start on a mouse click, because you will deliver the presentation in person.
   f.  On the final slide, use MLA style to list all the sources you used while researching and creating your presentation. ***Hint:*** *You may want to add your sources and create your Works Cited list in Word using commands and options in the Citations & Bibliography group on the References tab and then copy the information from Word to your final PowerPoint slide.*
   g.  On every slide except the title slide, insert a footer that includes a date that updates automatically, your name, and the slide number.

5 Apply a theme to the presentation.

6 Include speaker notes that you will use to deliver the presentation to the restaurant owner.

7 Save the presentation with the name **U7A1-A-Emenu-Lastname**, but replace *Lastname* with your last name.

8 Export the presentation to a Word document. **Hint:** *Click the File tab, click the Export option, and then click the Create Handouts option.* Save the exported document as **U7A1-A-Handouts-Lastname**, but replace Lastname with your last name.

### Steps, Part B

After you deliver your presentation on the benefits of an electronic menu and ordering system, the restaurant owner decides to implement an electronic system and asks you to identify possible vendors in your area. You go back online to research vendors. **Hint:** *Try search terms such as* electronic menu system vendors, electronic restaurant menu vendors, restaurant POS system, *and* digital menu boards.

1 Based on your online research, select at least three vendors. In an Excel worksheet, record the vendor name, address, and product name (that is, the name of the electronic menu and ordering system). **Hint:** *Use a separate column for each piece of information (field), such as* Street, City, Zip. Save the workbook as **U7A1-B-Emenu-Lastname**, but replace *Lastname* with your last name.

2 Start with a new, blank Word document or a Word letter template.

blank

3 Create a well-worded form letter that asks the vendor for more information about that vendor's product.
   a. Start with a heading that includes the current date, the name of the sender (the restaurant owner), and the name and address of the restaurant. **Hint:** *You can use information from a local restaurant or make up information.*
   b. Start a mail merge and connect to the data source (the worksheet created in Step 1). Insert merge fields at appropriate locations in the letter.
   c. Include your name in the closing of the letter.
   d. Save the letter as **U7A1-B-Emenu-Source-Lastname**, but replace *Lastname* with your last name.
   e. Merge the documents.

4 Save the merged letters as **U7A1-B-Emenu-Lastname**, but replace *Lastname* with your last name.

### Steps, Part C

Given all the information you have supplied, the restaurant owner decides to implement an electronic menu and ordering system. You are asked to create an Access database that contains names, descriptions, and prices for items that will be included in the electronic menu, and to create a database query that will display an order.

blank

1 Create a new, blank Access database and name it **U7A1-C-Emenu-Lastname**, but replace *Lastname* with your last name. **Hint:** *To create a new, blank desktop database, open Access, and then click the* Blank database *template in the Home backstage area.*

2 Create one table in the database, and name the table *Menu*.

3 The table needs the following fields. Select the appropriate data type and add a description for each field.
   *ItemName*
   *ItemDescription*
   *ItemCost*

*OrderedItem* (This field should contain *Yes* if the item is being ordered and should be empty otherwise.)

4   Enter the data for at least 20 menu items. Do not enter any data in the *OrderedItem* field. **Hint:** *You can use data from the menu of a local or online restaurant, or you can make up data.*

5   Create one query in the database, and name the query *Order*.

6   Set the query to select the item name and cost for each item marked *Yes* in the *OrderedItem* field. Save the Order query.

**Steps, Part D**

Eventually, the restaurant owner will add a feature that allows customers to pay using a debit or credit card and prints a simple itemized receipt. However, that feature will not be available when you pilot the new system. For the pilot, you are asked to create an Excel workbook that displays a bill for an order on one sheet tab and a chart comparing the costs of the items ordered on a second sheet tab. The chart worksheet will be made available to customers to make it easy to see how to split the cost of a bill based on the item price.

1   Open the Access database you created in Part C of this project, named **U7A1-C-Emenu-Lastname** (where *Lastname* is replaced by your last name), type Yes in three items in the *OrderedItem* field, save the query, and then run the Order query.

blank

2   Open a new, blank Excel workbook and copy the rows from the Access Order query result into a blank worksheet beginning at row 3.

3   In row 1 of the worksheet, type the name of the restaurant. If necessary, adjust the column width and row height.

4   In row 2, type the column heading Item for column A, and type the column heading Cost for column B. Delete row 3, which contains the column headings from the Access data.

5   Below the order information you inserted in Step 2, compute the order total using a function.

6   Below the total, compute three tip options as follows:
    a. Display the tip amount at 15%, 18%, and 20% of the total.
    b. Also show the total bill amount with tip for each of the three options.

7   Format the worksheet using appropriate alignment and number and text formats.

8   Size the columns and rows and add color, borders, and other visual formatting to make the worksheet easier to read.

9   On a separate sheet in the same workbook, create a pie chart that compares the various costs of the items ordered. Enhance the pie chart as follows:
    a. Add a chart title.
    b. Label the slices with the cost and the percent.

10  Name the worksheet containing the data *Customer Bill* and the worksheet containing the pie chart *Order Comparison*.

11  Add a footer to both worksheets. In the footer, type your name and today's date.

12  Save the Excel workbook as **U7A1-D-Emenu-Lastname**, but replace *Lastname* with your last name.